Simple Methods for

Identification of Plastics

Dietrich Braun

With the Plastics Identification Table
by Hansjürgen Saechtling

Second Edition

Distributed in the United States of America
by Macmillan Publishing Co., Inc., New York

Distributed in Canada
by Collier Macmillan Canada, Ltd., Toronto

HANSER
PUBLISHERS

Prof. Dr. rer. nat. Dietrich Braun
Deutsches Kunststoff-Institut, Schloßgartenstr. 6 R, D-6100 Darmstadt

Dr. Hansjürgen Saechtling
Consulting chemist for plastics technology and application GDCh-VDI-Teli
Wilhelm-Beer-Weg 103, D-6000 Frankfurt am Main

Translated by Dr. Edmund Immergut
2 Sydney Place, Brooklyn, N.Y. 11201, USA

Distributed in USA by
Scientific and Technical Books Macmillan Publishing Co., Inc.
866 Third Avenue, New York, N.Y. 10022

Distributed in Canada by
Collier Macmillan Canada Distribution Center
539 Collier Macmillian Drive, Cambridge, Ontario

Distributed in all other countries by
Carl Hanser Verlag, Kolbergerstr. 22, D-8000 München 80

The use of general descriptive names, trademarks, etc, in this publication, even if the former are not especially identified, is not to be taken as a sign that such names, as understood by the Trade Marks and Merchandise Marks Act, may accordingly be used freely by anyone.

While the advice and information in this book are believed to be true and accurate at the date of going to press, neither the authors nor the editors nor the publisher can accept any legal responsibility for any errors or omissions that may be made. The publisher makes no warranty, express or implied, with respect to the material contained herein.

Braun, Dietrich:
Simple methods for identification of plastics /
Dietrich Braun. With the Plastics identification
table / by Hansjürgen Saechtling. [Transl. by
Edmund Immergut]. – 2. ed. – München; Wien: Hanser,
1986.
   Dt. Ausg. u. d. T.: Braun, Dietrich:
   Erkennen von Kunststoffen
   ISBN 3-446-14855-8

NE: Saechtling, Hansjürgen: Plastics
identification table

ISBN 3-446-14855-8   Carl Hanser Verlag München Wien
ISBN 0-02-949261-0   Macmillan Publishing Co., Inc., New York

Library of Congress Catalog Card Number 86-063089

Cover design: C. A. Loipersberger

Preface to the Second Edition

The First Edition of this small analysis book was well received by users and reviewers; it has also been translated into several languages. This shows that inspite of all the modern, and unfortunately often quite expensive, analytical methods and advances in the field of instrumental analysis, there still exists a need for simple methods for the identification of plastics.

The Second Edition, therefore, did not require very substantial changes. A table on polymer blends was added because these materials have become important industrially. Some additional tests were added to Chapter 6 which describes specific identification tests for different types of plastics. Chapter 5, on systematic analytical procedures, was enlarged and now incorporates the Plastics Identification Table of Dr. Hansjürgen Saechtling (currently in its 8th Edition). I am grateful to Dr. Saechtling for agreeing to the inclusion of his table in my book and also for his advice and suggestions concerning additions and revisions of the text.

With this edition, as with the earlier one, I owe thanks to Hanser Publishers (Carl Hanser Verlag) and especially to Dr. W. Glenz for their excellent cooperation during the production of this book. I also repeat my invitation to the users of the book to write me about their experiences with these analytical procedures and to send me suggestions for additions or improvements.

Darmstadt, Autumn 1986   Dietrich Braun

Preface to the First Edition

Processors and users of plastics often need to determine the chemical nature of a plastics sample. In contrast to the producers of plastics, however, they usually lack specially equipped laboratories and a staff with analytical experience.

The complete identification of a high molecular weight organic compound is often a rather complicated problem which can sometimes be solved only with the expenditure of a considerable amount of effort. For many practical situations it is often quite sufficient to determine the class of plastics to which an unknown sample belongs, for example, whether it is a polyolefin or a polyamide. To answer such questions one need have only relatively simple means at hand and some rudimentary knowledge of chemistry.

Several more or less comprehensive sets of instructions for carrying out simple analyses of plastics may be found in the literature. These include the Plastics Identification Table by Hansjürgen Saechtling (8th edition by Carl Hanser Publishers, 1979), which since many years has been a valuable instruction for the identification of plastics starting from their appearance. With the kind permission of the author the table has been included in this book. However, some of these are rather brief and others are experimentally too demanding. Many simpler testing methods are also scattered throughout the technical literature and are not always easily accessible.

I have therefore tried to collect in this book a selection of procedures from the literature and from my own years of experience. These are intended to enable the technician, the engineer, or the technical salesperson to identify unknown plastic materials. Of course, one cannot expect such simple methods to yield a high degree of information. Therefore one has to limit oneself to the identification of the plastic material; the analysis of fillers, plasticizers, stabilizers, or other additives, which are often present only in very small amounts, requires more extensive physical or chemical methods. It should also be pointed out that many' industrial combinations of materials or copolymers cannot always be identified with simple methods. In such cases it is necessary to use more advanced methods of analysis.

This book does not require in-depth chemical knowledge, only a certain ability to carry out simple laboratory operations. I particularly remind the reader to use care in the handling of chemicals, solvents, and open flames. Special safety measures that have to be taken into account are pointed out at pertinent places in the book. The necessary equipment is listed in Chapter 8. It is useful in most of these tests to carry out comparative experiments with samples of known plastics. A collection of plastics samples is available from the Society of Plastics Engineers, Brookfield Center, CT 06805.

I have carried out all the tests mentioned in this book and have used them in teaching a number of courses.

That experience has been called upon in writing these chapters. Comments or recommendations for additions from readers of this book are most welcome.

We hope that this manual will close the gap between the rather large and complicated books on the analysis of plastics, which require an extensive background in chemistry and physics, and the various tabular compilations which usually limit themselves to certain preliminary testing. Of course, this requires a consideration of the compromise between the experimental effort and the efficient yield of simple qualitative analytical procedures.

The development and testing of simple methods for the analysis of plastic materials was the subject of a research project of the German Plastics Institute carried out with the financial support of the Arbeitsgemeinschaft Industrieller Forschungs-Vereinigungen e.V. In this program there were several collaborators whom I want to thank, especially Dr. J. Arndt, who helped me in putting the text together. I also thank Dr. W. Glenz for many valuable recommendations and Dr. E. Immergut for his careful translation of this book.

Darmstadt, Spring 1982   Dietrich Braun

Contents

Plastics Identification Table
see inside back cover pocket

1 Plastics and Their Appearance

Plastics are high molecular weight (macromolecular or polymeric) organic substances that have usually been synthesized from low molecular weight compounds. They may also have been obtained by chemical modification of high molecular weight natural materials (especially cellulose). The raw materials are most often petroleum, natural gas, and coal. They can be reacted with air, water, or sodium chloride to prepare reactive monomers. The most important industrial synthetic processes for the preparation of plastics from monomers may be classified according to the mechanism of the formation reaction of the polymer, such as polymerization and condensation reactions. Since several chemically identical or similar plastics can be prepared in several different ways and from different raw materials, this classification has little meaning for the analysis of unknown plastics samples. On the other hand, in addition to chemical investigations, the appearance of a plastic as well as its behavior on heating yields useful information for its identification.

There are physical interactions between the individual macromolecules that constitute a plastic material, just as there are between the molecules of a low molecular weight compound. These physical interactions are responsible for cohesion and related properties such as strength, hardness, and softening behavior. Plastics that consist of linear threadlike molecules (several hundred nanometers (nm) long and a few

tenths of a nanometer in diameter) or of macromolecules that are not strongly crosslinked can usually
be softened on heating. In many cases they melt. Thus,
when a polymeric material is heated above a certain
temperature, the macromolecules which are more or
less oriented with respect to each other at low temperatures can glide past each other to form a melt of relatively high viscosity. Depending on the degree of order
of the macromolecule in the solid state, it is possible to
distinguish between partly crystalline and (mostly dis-
ordered) amorphous plastics (see Fig. 1). This degree

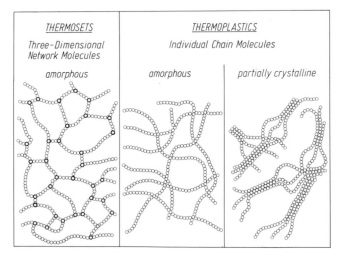

Figure 1. Schematic representation of the structure of plastics, show-
ing the three major types of macromolecular arrangements. Approximately 1,000,000 times actual size and greatly simplified. (Crystal-
lites can also occur as the result of chain folding.)

of order also has an effect on the behavior of the plastic on heating and on its solubility.

Plastics that soften on heating and start to flow are called thermoplastics. On cooling, such plastics become solid again. This process can be repeated many times. There are several exceptions, as when the chemical stability (expressed in terms of the temperature at which chemical decomposition starts) is lower than the cohesion between the macromolecules due to interaction between the chains, in which case, on heating, the plastic undergoes chemical changes before it reaches its softening or melting point. A further indication, with few exceptions, that macromolecules are linear or branched is their solubility in many liquids, such as organic solvents. This process also affects the interaction between the macromolecules; solvent molecules insert themselves between the polymer chains.

In contrast to thermoplastic materials, there are the so-called thermosetting materials. These, after processing into their final state, are crosslinked macromolecules that can neither melt nor dissolve. For such products one generally starts with liquid or soluble raw materials of a rather low molecular weight. These may be crosslinked by heating with or without pressure or through chemical reactions with additives and concurrent molding conditions. The results are crosslinked (hardened) high molecular weight materials in threedimensional networks. These giant molecules can be broken down into smaller and therefore meltable and soluble fragments only by chemical destruction of the crosslinks. This may occur at rather high temperatures or with certain chemical reagents. Thermosets often contain fillers that may strongly influence the appearance and properties of the products.

Finally, from their physical appearance, we may distinguish the elastomers, rubberlike elastic materials

consisting of usually relatively weakly crosslinked macromolecules. Crosslinkages of natural or synthetic rubber are formed during the molding or vulcanization
process. Because of their crosslinked nature, elastomers do not melt on heating until just below their
decomposition temperature. In this sense they behave
differently from many other elastic thermoplastic
materials such as plasticized polyvinyl chloride.

Table 1 lists the most important characteristics of
these three groups of polymeric materials. In addition
to elasticity, behavior on heating, density, and solubility can be used to differentiate between these materials. However, it should be kept in mind that fillers,
pigments, or reinforcing agents, for example, carbon
black or glass fibers, lead to considerable deviations
from these properties. Therefore it is not always possible to identify polymeric materials on the basis of
these criteria. The densities listed in Table 1 are only
rough approximations for some solid materials. For
example, foams have densities of approximately 0.1 g/
cm^3 or less. Structural foams with integral skin and
cellular core have densities between 0.2 and 0.9 g/cm^3
and often cannot be recognized as foams from their
outer appearance.

It is not possible to discuss here the special properties of all the different types of plastic materials that
can occur within the main groups. The plastics industry
today, by employing copolymerization or chemical
modification, is capable of producing an extraordinary
number of combinations of properties, making the
identification of corresponding plastics more complicated. Its physical appearance and its classification as a
thermoplastic, thermoset, or elastomer therefore permit us to draw conclusions about the chemical nature
of the plastic only in simple cases. But they often pro-

vide a useful additional way of characterizing the material.

In the last few years a number of products consisting of a mixture of different plastics have made their appearance; they are usually called polymer blends and polymer alloys. Their identification using simple methods presents considerable difficulties because flame tests and pyrolysis tests are usually not unambiguous. Also a separation into different groups according to the pH-value of the pyrolysates does not permit a definite conclusion. In some cases it is possible to separate polymer mixtures into their components if these have different solubility characteristics and then to identify the components. However it is not possible to recommend a generally applicable separation procedure.

The examination of mixtures of polyamides and polyolefins is relatively easy because the polyamide component can be degraded by acid hydrolysis and the resulting low molecular weight fragments can be identified according to the procedure described in Section 6.2.10. Table 5 lists some of the most importat polymer blends together with their trade names and suppliers.

Although synthetic fibers and synthetic elastomers have the same chemical structure as plastics, they are not included among the latter group. Their identification will therefore be treated in this book only if they also occur as plastics. For example, polycaprolactam (nylon 6) is used both for fiber production and as a molding material.

Tables 2–5 contain a compilation of the plastics discussed in this volume, their chemical abbreviations, and some selected trade names. An extensive table of polymer acronyms on ASTM, DIN and ISO standards can be found on pages 100–105 (Chapter 10).

Table 1. Comparison of Different Classes of Plastics

	Structure	Physical Appearance*	Density (g/cm³)	Behavior on Heating	Behavior on Treating with Solvents
Thermo-plastics	Linear or branched macromolecules	Partially crystalline: flexible to horn-like; hazy, milky to opaque; only thin films are transparent	0.9–1.4 (except PTFE: 2–2.3)	Material softens; fusible and becomes clear on melting; often fibers can be drawn from the melt; heat-seal-able (exceptions exist)	May swell; usually difficult to dissolve in cold solvents, but usually readily dissolved on heating the solvent, e.g., polyethylene in xylene
		Amorphous: colorless; clear and transparent without additives; hard to rubbery (e.g., on adding plasticizers)	0.9–1.9		Soluble (with few exceptions) in certain organic solvents, usually after initial swelling

Thermosets (after processing)	(Usually) tightly crosslinked macromolecules	Hard; usually contain fillers and are opaque. Without fillers they are transparent	1.2–1.4; filled: 1.4–2.0	Remain hard; almost dimensionally stable until chemical decomposition sets in	Insoluble, do not swell or only slightly
Elastomers	(Usually) lightly crosslinked macromolecules	Rubber-elastic and stretchable	0.8–1.3	Do not flow until close to temperature where chemical decomposition occurs	Insoluble, but will often swell

* A rough measure for the hardness of a plastic is its behavior on scratching with a fingernail: hard plastics scratch the nail; hornlike plastics have about the same hardness; flexible or rubbery plastics can be scratched or dented with a fingernail.

Table 2. Thermoplastics

Chemical or Technical Name	Abbreviation (Acronym)	Repeating Unit	Selected Trade Names (Registered Trademarks)
Polyolefins			
Polyethylene	PE	$-CH_2-CH_2-$	Alkathene, Dowlex, Escorene, Hostalen, Lupolen, Marlex, Alathon, Paxon
Ethylene Copolymers	EEA EVA	With ethyl acrylate With vinyl acetate	Primacor, Lucalen Elvax, Ultrathene
Chlorinated polyethylene	PEC	Sulfochlorinated	Hypalon
Polypropylene	PP	$-CH_2-CH-$ CH_3	Pro-Fax PP, Hostalen PP, Escorene, Fortilene, Moplen, Novolen, Rexene PP
Polybutene-1	PB	$-CH_2-CH-$ CH_2-CH_3 CH_3	Witron
Polyisobutylene	PIB	$-CH_2-C-$ CH_3 CH_3	Vistanex

			(Mitsui Petrochem.)
Poly-4-methylpentene-1	PMP	$-CH_2-CH-CH_2-CH-CH_3$ $\quad\quad\quad\quad\quad CH_3$	TPX
Styrene Polymers and Copolymers			
Polystyrene	PS	$-CH_2-CH-$ ⬡	Hostyren, Lustrex, Styron
Modified polystyrene (high impact)	SB	Graft copolymers with polybutadiene or with EPDM-rubber	K-Resin, Styrolux
Styrene copolymers	SAN	With acrylonitrile	Luran, Lustran, Tyril
ABS	ABS	Terpolymers: AN, BD, St	Cycolac, Lustran, Terluran
ASA	ASA	Terpolymers: AN, St, acrylate	Luran
Halogen-Containing Polymers			
Polyvinyl chloride	PVC	$-CH_2-CH-$ $\quad\quad\quad Cl$	Dural, Geon, Hostalit, Vestolit, Vinnol, Corvic, Benvic
Modified PVC (high impact)	—	With EVA copolymers (EVA/VC graft copolymers) With chlorinated polyethylene With polyacrylate	Levapren VC Hostalit H, Z Acryloid

(continued)

Table 2. Thermoplastics (continued)

Chemical or Technical Name	Abbreviation (Acronym)	Repeating Unit	Selected Trade names (Registered Trademarks)
Halogen-Containing Polymers (continued)			
Polyvinylidene chloride	PVDC	$-CH_2-CCl_2-$	Saran
Polytetrafluoroethylene	PTFE	$-CF_2-CF_2-$	Teflon, Fluon, Halon, Hostaflon
Polytetrafluoroethylene copolymers	PETFE PFEP	Copolymers with ethylene Copolymers with hexafluoropropylene	Tefzel
Polytrifluorochloro-ethylene	PCTFE	$-CF_2-\underset{Cl}{CF}-$	Kel-F, Fluorothene
Trifluorochloroethylene copolymers	PECTFE	Copolymers with ethylene	Halar
Perfluoroalkoxy-polymers	PFA	$-CF_2-CF_2-\underset{O}{CF}-CF_2-$ OR	Teflon
Polyvinyl fluoride	PVF	$-CH_2-\underset{F}{CH}-$	Tedlar, Kynar
Polyvinylidene fluoride	PVDF	$-CH_2-CF_2-$	Floraflon, Kynar, Solef

Poly(meth)acrylates			
Polyacrylonitrile	PAN	$-CH_2-CH-$ $\quad\quad CN$	Orlon, Acrilan, Barex, Lopac (copolymers with styrene)
Polyacrylates	–	$-CH_2-CH-$ $\quad\quad COOR$ R from different alcohols	
Polymethyl methacrylate	PMMA	$\quad\quad CH_3$ $-CH_2-C-$ $\quad\quad COOCH_3$	Plexiglas, Perspex, Lucite, Acrylite
Methyl methacrylate copolymers	AMMA	Copolymers with AN	
Polymers with Hetero-atom Chain Structure			
Polyoxymethylene	POM	$-CH_2-O-$	Delrin, Celcon, Ultraform, Hostaform
Polyphenylene oxide	PPO/PPE	$\quad CH_3$ $\quad O-$ $\quad CH_3$	Noryl
Modified PPO/PPE		With polystyrene	Noryl, Luranyl, Prevex

(continued)

Table 2. Thermoplastics (continued)

Chemical or Technical Name	Abbreviation (Acronym)	Repeating Unit	Selected Trade Names (Registered Trademarks)
Polymers with Heteroatom Chain Structure (continued)			
Polycarbonate	PC	[structure: phenyl–C(CH$_3$)$_2$–phenyl–O–CO–O–]	Lexan, Makrolon, Merlon
Polyethylene terephthalate	PET	$-CH_2-CH_2-O-CO-$[benzene]$-CO-O-$	Dacron, Mylar, Tenite, Rynite
Polybutylene terephthalate	PBT	$-(CH_2-CH_2)_2-O-CO-$[benzene]$-CO-O-$	Celanex, Pocan, Tenite, Valox
Polyamide	PA		
Nylon 6	PA 6	$-NH(CH_2)_5CO-$	Capron, Grilon, Nydur, Ultramid
Nylon 6,6	PA 66	$-NH(CH_2)_6NH-CO(CH_2)_4CO-$	Zytel, Vydyne, Technyl, Ultramid
Nylon 6,10	PA 610	$-NH(CH_2)_6NH-CO(CH_2)_8CO-$	Nylafil
Nylon 11	PA 11	$-NH(CH_2)_{10}CO-$	Rilsan B

Nylon 12	PA 12	$-NH(CH_2)_{11}CO-$	Rilsan A, Vestamid
Aromatic PA		With terephthalic acid	Aramid
Polyphenylene sulfide	PPS		Ryton, Thermocomp OF
Polysulfone	PSU		Udel
Polyethersulfone	PES		Ultrason, Victrex
Cellulose			
acetate (R = H)	CA		Tenite
acetobutyrate (R = COCH_3)	CAB		Tenite, Urex
propionate (R = CO-CH_2-CH_3)	CP		Tenite
nitrate (R = NO_2)	CN		
Methyl cellulose (R = CH_3)	MC		Forticel
Ethyl cellulose (R = C_2H_5)	EC		
Vulcanized Fiber (Regenerated cellulose/resin laminate)	VF		Hornex

(continued)

Table 2. Thermoplastics (continued)

Chemical or Technical Name	Abbreviation (Acronym)	Repeating Unit	Selected Trade Names (Registered Trademarks)
Resins, Dispersions and Other Specialty Products			
Polyvinyl acetate	PVAC	$-CH_2-CH-$ $\quad\quad O-CO-CH_3$	Elvacet, Gelva, Vinylite
Vinyl acetate copolymers		VA/maleinate VA/versatate VA/acrylate VA/ethylene	Elvacet, Gelva
Polyvinyl alcohol	PVAL	$-CH_2-CH-$ $\quad\quad OH$	Elvanol, Gelvatol
Polyvinyl ether		$-CH_2-CH-$ $\quad\quad OR$ R = different radicals	Lutonal
Polyvinyl acetal	PVB PVFO	With butyraldehyde With formaldehyde	Butvar, Butacite PVB Formvar

Silicone	SI	$\begin{array}{c} \text{R} \\ -\text{Si}-\text{O}- \\ \text{R} \end{array}$ R = e.g., CH_3	Silastic, GE, Dow Corning (Resins, coating resins, oils, elastomers under different names, some may be hardened)
Casein	CS	$-NH-CO-$ (polypeptide from milk albumin crosslinked with formaldehyde)	

Table 3. Thermosets

Chemical or Technical Designation	Abbreviation (Acronym)	Starting Materials	Reactive Groups* or Curing Agent	Intermediate Products and Curing Procedures
Phenoplasts			$-CH_2OH;$	Novolacs (not self-curing; cured, e.g., by addition of hexamethylenetetramine)
Phenolic resins	PF	Phenol (R = H) and substituted phenols (e.g., cresols and formaldehyde)	OH R (benzene ring with OH and R)	Resoles (cured under pressure and heating, sometimes with catalysts, to Resits)
Cresol-formaldehyde resins	CF	Cresol (R=CH$_3$) and formaldehyde		
Aminoplasts				
Urea-formaldehyde resins	UF	Urea (sometimes also thiourea) and formaldehyde	$-NH_2;$ $-NH-CH_2OH;$	Intermediate products in the form of aqueous solutions or solids; curing occurs under pressure and heating, sometimes using acid catalysts
Melamine-formaldehyde resins	MF	Melamine and formaldehyde	$-N(CH_2OH)_2$	

Unsaturated polyester resins	UP	Polyesters with unsaturated dicarboxylic acids, usually maleic acid, and saturated acids such as succinic acid, adipic acid, phthalic acid, and diols such as butanediol	$-CO-CH=CH-CO-$	Polyesters are usually dissolved in styrene, seldom in other monomers; curing by radical copolymerization using hot- or cold-type catalysts
Glass fiber-reinforced unsaturated polyester resins	GUP or GF-UP			
Epoxy resins	EP	From di- or polyols or bisphenols and epichlorohydrin or other epoxide-forming components	$-CH-CH-$ O	Liquid or solid intermediates that are cured either hot, e.g., using dicarboxylic acids or anhydrides, or cold using, e.g., di- or polyamines
Polyurethanes	PUR	Di- or polyisocyanates react with diols or polyols to form crosslinked hard or soft (usually elastic) products	$-N=C=O + HO-$ $-NH-CO-O-$	Isocyanates (e.g., MDI, TDI, Desmodur) and OH-containing compounds (different polyols) are reacted in the liquid or molten state

* Since the chemical composition of crosslinked plastics cannot be given with any accuracy, this table lists starting materials and reactive groups but does not describe the products or give the trade names of the many available thermosets that differ in composition as well as content of additives, e.g., fillers.

Table 4. Elastomers*

Chemical or Technical Designation	Abbreviation (Acronym)	Starting Materials	Typical Repeating Units	
Polybutadiene	BR	Butadiene	$-CH_2-CH=CH-CH_2-$	1,4-Addition (*cis* or *trans*)
			$-CH_2-CH-$ $\quad\quad CH=CH_2$	1,2-Addition (isotactic, syndiotactic, or atactic)
Polychloroprene (Neoprene, Perbunan)	CR	Chloroprene	$-CH_2-C=CH-CH_2-$ $\quad\quad Cl$	Structural isomers exist
Polyisoprene	PIP NR	Isoprene Natural rubber	$-CH_2-C=CH-CH_2-$ $\quad\quad CH_3$	*cis*-1,4-Polyisoprene (Guttapercha or balata: *trans*-1,4-Polyisoprene)

Nitrile rubber	NBR	Acrylonitrile and butadiene
Styrene-butadiene rubber	SBR	Styrene and butadiene
Butyl rubber	IIR	Isobutylene and a small amount of isoprene
Ethylene-propylene rubber	EPM	Ethylene and propylene
	EPDM or EPD	Terpolymers with dienes
Fluorine rubber	FE	Fluorine-containing olefins
Chlorohydrin rubber	CHR	Epichlorohydrin-ethylene oxide copolymers
Propylene oxide rubber	POR	Copolymer from propylene oxide and allyl glycidyl ether

* This table contains only a selection of the most important elastomers. Their structure is shown in the unvulcanized state.

Table 5. Polymer Blends

Polymer Blends*	Trade Name	Supplier
ABS/PVC	Abson	Goodrich Chemical Co.
	Cycoloy EH	Borg-Warner Chemicals
	Cycovin KAB	Borg-Warner Chemicals
	Kralastic FVM	USS Chemicals
	Polyman 509	A. Schulman GmbH
ABS/TPU	Cycoloy	Borg-Warner Chemicals
	Estane	Goodrich Chemical Co.
	Pellethane	Upjohn Polymer Chemical Div.
PA-Blends	Beetle AC1	BIP Chemical Ltd.
	Durethan VP KL 1-2311	Bayer AG
	6 Polyloy BC 80	Dr. Illing GmbH
	Schulamid	A. Schulman GmbH
	Zytel	E. I. Du Pont de Nemours
PBTB/PB	Pocan S 1506	Bayer AG
PC/ABS	Bayblend	Bayer AG
	Cycolac	Borg-Warner Chemicals
	Cycoloy	Borg-Warner Chemicals
	Moldex A	Anic S. p. A.
	Polyman HT	A. Schulman GmbH
PC/PBTP	Makroblend	Bayer AG
	Xenoy CL 100	General Electric Co.
PC/HIPS	Bayblend H	Bayer AG
PETP/PC	Ropet	Rohm & Haas Co.
PI/PPS	Tribolon	Tribolon Industries Fluoroplastics
	Upjohn 2080	Upjohn Polymer Chemicals Div.

Table 5. Polymer Blends (continued)

Polymer Blends*	Trade Name	Supplier
PMMA/PC	Diakon	ICI
PMMA/PVC	Acrylivin	General Tire & Rubber Co.
	Kydex	Rohm & Haas Co.
POM/ Elastomer	Delrin T, ST Ultraform N2640X	E. I. Du Pont de Nemours BASF AG
PP/EPDM	Hostalen PP Vestolen EM	Hoechst AG Hüls AG
PPO/PPE/PA	Noryl GTX Ultranyl	General Electric Co. BASF
PPO/PPE/PS	Noryl Prevex	General Electric Co. Borg-Warner Chemicals
	Ultranyl	BASF
PPSU/ABS	Mindel	Union Carbide
PPSU/SAN	Ucardel	Union Carbide

* For identification of the polymers in these blends see the list of polymer acronyms on pages 100–105.

2 General Introduction to the Analysis of Plastics

2.1 Analytical Procedure

Each plastic analysis begins with preliminary tests. In addition to the observation of several characteristics such as solubility, density, softening, and melting behavior, an important role is played by heating in a combustion tube (pyrolysis test) and in an open flame (flame test). If these preliminary tests do not yield a positive identification, examine the materials for the presence of heteroatoms such as nitrogen, halogens (especially chlorine and fluorine), and sulfur. Then begin a systematic analysis by testing the solubility, and proceed to simple specific tests. In addition, try to identify the possible presence of organic or inorganic fillers or other additives such as plasticizers or stabilizers. Unfortunately, the simple approaches discussed here seldom give reliable information about the type and amounts of such additives.

As an aid in the identification of the type of plastic used in semifinished plastic materials or in plastic moldings, the "Plastics Identification Table" by Dr. Hj. Saechtling included in this book has proved to be quite useful. Starting from the appearance of the material and its elastic behavior, the table leads to a series of simple tests which allow further differentiation between types of plastics. Procedures used in these tests, mentioned in the headings of the table, are described in detail at appropriate places in the text of this book. For such tests it is sufficient to take small splinters or

filings removed from the sample at some inconspicu-
ous place.

2.2   Sample Preparation

Plastics as a raw material usually are in the form of
powders, granules, and very occasionally dispersions.
After processing, they are usually encountered as
films, plates, profiles, or molded products.

Some preliminary tests, for example, a flame test,
can be carried out on the original form (granules,
chips, etc.). For most tests, however, it is better if the
sample is available in a finely divided or powdery state.
To reduce the size of the particles, use a mill; a coffee
grinder may be sufficient. On thorough chilling by
adding dry ice (solid CO_2), most tough or elastic materials become brittle and can be ground. The chilling
prevents them from becoming overheated during the
grinding process.

Very often, processed plastic materials contain
additives: plasticizers, stabilizers, fillers, or coloring
agents such as pigments. Such additives usually do not
interfere with the simple, not very specific, preliminary
tests. For a quantitative determination or for the definite identification of a plastic material, the additives
must first be removed. For this purpose, extraction
(see Fig. 2) or precipitation methods are used. Processing aids such as stabilizers or lubricants similar to plasticizers can usually be extracted with ether or other
organic solvents. If an extraction apparatus (Soxhlet) is
not available, it may be sufficient to shake the finely
divided sample with ether or to heat the sample in
ether for several hours under reflux. Use extreme caution. Ether is flammable. Do not use an open flame.

Linear polymers can be separated from fillers or reinforcing agents (glass fibers or carbon black) by dissolving them in suitable solvents. (For the selection of solvents, see Section 3.1.) All insoluble material then remains behind and can be isolated by filtration. The dissolved polymer can be reprecipitated by adding the solution dropwise to a 5–10 times larger volume of the precipitating agent. As a precipitating agent, methanol is usually suitable. In some cases water can be the precipitating agent.

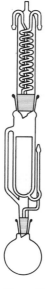

Crosslinked plastics cannot be separated from fillers in this way due to their insolubility. Inorganic fillers (glass fibers or chalk) can sometimes be isolated by burning the sample in a porcelain cup, although this is not always the case. Carbon black may also burn off. However, it is frequently necessary to use special methods, which vary from case to case.

Figure 2. Soxhlet extractor. The extraction liquid is heated to boiling in a round-bottom flask, and the resulting vapor is condensed in a reflux condenser mounted at the top of the extractor. From the condenser the liquid drops onto the solid sample in the cup. When the liquid in the extractor vessel reaches the exit tube near the top (right side of the extractor) it flows back into the round-bottom flask. The solvent must have a lower specific gravity than the material being extracted (otherwise the sample would float out of the extractor cup).

3 Preliminary Tests

3.1 Solubility

Among the many solvents for plastics, the most widely used are benzene, tetrahydrofuran, dimethylformamide, diethyl ether, acetone, and formic acid. In certain cases, chloroethylene, ethyl acetate, ethanol, and water are also useful. Tables 6 and 7 show a compilation of the behavior of the most important plastics in various solvents. For the systematic analysis of plastics, the distinction between soluble and insoluble polymers provides a first separation into two groups. We can then apply chemical methods to investigate these two groups further.

For the determination of solubility, add approximately 0.1 g of the finely divided plastic to a test tube with 5–10 ml of the solvent. Over the course of several hours, thoroughly shake the test tube and observe the possible swelling of the sample. This can often take quite a long while. If necessary, heat the test tube gently with constant agitation. This can be done with a Bunsen burner, but a water bath is better. Great care must be employed to avoid sudden boiling up of the solvent and having it spray out of the test tube, since most organic solvents or their vapors are flammable. If the solubility test leaves doubts and/or if insoluble particles (glass fibers or inorganic fillers) remain behind, they must be removed. They can be most easily filtered or decanted after the solution has been allowed to

stand overnight. For the test, evaporating a part of the
supernatant liquid on a watchglass leaves the dissolved
material as a residue. The filtered solution can also be
dropped into a nonsolvent for that particular plastic,
in which case dissolved polymer will precipitate.
Petroleum ether or methanol and occasionally water
are used as precipitating agents.

The solubility of a plastic material depends very
much on its chemical structure and to some extent
on its molecular weight. The solvents mentioned in
Table 7, therefore, do not always permit an unambiguous identification.

Table 6. Solubility of Plastics

Polymer	Solvent	Nonsolvent
Polyethylene, polybutene-1, isotactic polypropylene	p-Xylene*, trichlorobenzene*, decane*, decalin*	Acetone, diethyl ether, lower alcohols
Atactic polypropylene	Hydrocarbons, isoamyl acetate	Ethyl acetate, propanol
Polyisobutylene	Hexane, benzene, carbon tetrachloride, tetrahydrofuran	Acetone, methanol, methyl acetate
Polybutadiene, polyisoprene	Aliphatic and aromatic hydrocarbons	Acetone, diethyl ether, lower alcohols
Polystyrene	Benzene, toluene, chloroform, cyclohexanone, butyl acetate, carbon disulfide	Lower alcohols, diethyl ether (swells)
Polyvinyl chloride	Tetrahydrofuran, cyclohexanone, methyl ethyl ketone, dimethyl formamide	Methanol, acetone, heptane
Polyvinyl fluoride	Cyclohexanone, dimethyl formamide	Aliphatic hydrocarbons, methanol
Polytetrafluoroethylene	Insoluble	—
Polyvinyl acetate	Benzene, chloroform, methanol, acetone, butyl acetate	Diethyl ether, petroleum ether, butanol

Table 6. Solubility of Plastics (continued)

Polymer	Solvent	Nonsolvent
Polyvinyl isobutyl ether	Isopropanol, methyl ethylene ketone, chloroform, aromatic hydrocarbons	Methanol, acetone
Polyacrylates and polymethacrylates	Chloroform, acetone, ethyl acetate, tetrahydrofuran, toluene	Methanol, diethyl ether, petroleum ether
Polyacrylonitrile	Dimethylformamide, dimethylsulfoxide, concentrated sulfuric acid	Alcohols, diethyl ether, water, hydrocarbons
Polyacrylamide	Water	Methanol, acetone
Polyacrylic acid	Water, dilute alkalies, methanol, dioxane, dimethylformamide	Hydrocarbons, methanol, acetone, diethyl ether
Polyvinyl alcohol	Water, dimethylformamide*, dimethylsulfoxide*	Hydrocarbons, methanol, acetone, diethyl ether
Cellulose	Aqueous cupriammonium hydroxide, aqueous zinc chloride, aqueous calcium thiocyanate	Methanol, acetone
Cellulose diacetate	Acetone	Methylene chloride
Cellulose triacetate	Methylene chloride, chloroform, dioxane	Methanol, diethyl ether

Methyl cellulose (trimethyl)	Chloroform, benzene	Ethanol, diethyl ether, petroleum ether
Carboxymethyl cellulose	Water	Methanol
Aliphatic polyesters	Chloroform, formic acid, benzene	Methanol, diethyl ether, aliphatic hydrocarbons
Polyethylene glycol terephthalate	m-Cresol, o-chlorophenol, nitrobenzene, trichloroacetic acid	Methanol, acetone, aliphatic hydrocarbons
Polyamides	Formic acid, conc. sulfuric acid, dimethylformamide, m-cresol	Methanol, diethyl ether, hydrocarbons
Polyurethanes (uncrosslinked)	Formic acid, γ-butyrolactone, dimethylformamide, m-cresol	Methanol, diethyl ether, hydrocarbons
Polyoxymethylene	γ-Butyrolactone*, dimethylformamide*, benzyl alcohol*	Methanol, diethyl ether, aliphatic hydrocarbons
Polyethylene oxide	Water, benzene, dimethylformamide	Aliphatic hydrocarbons, diethyl ether
Polydimethylsiloxane	Chloroform, heptane, benzene, diethyl ether	Methanol, ethanol

* Often soluble only at elevated temperatures.

Table 7. Plastics Dissolved by Selected Solvents

Water	Tetrahydrofuran (THF)	Boiling Xylene	Dimethyl-formamide (DMF)	Formic Acid	Insoluble in all of these solvents
Polyacrylamide Polyvinyl alcohol Polyvinyl methyl ether Polyethylene oxide Polyvinyl-pyrrolidone Polymaleic anhydride	All uncross-linked polymers*	Polyolefins Styrene polymers Vinyl chloride polymers Polyacrylates Polytrifluoro-chloroethylene	Polyacrylo-nitrile Polyformaldehyde (in boiling DMF)	Polyamides Polyvinyl alcohol derivatives Urea- and melamine-formaldehyde condensates (uncured)	Polyfluoro hydrocarbons Polyethylene terephthalate** Crosslinked (cured, vulcanized) polymers

* Except polyolefins, polyfluoro hydrocarbons, polyacrylamide, polyformaldehyde, polyamides, polyurethanes, urea and melamine resins.

** Soluble in nitrobenzene.

3.2   Density

The density, ϱ, is the quotient of mass M and volume V of a material

$$\varrho = \frac{M}{V} \text{ g/cm}^3$$

With plastics the density is seldom useful as a means of characterization. Many processed plastics contain hollow spaces, pores, or imperfections. In such cases (for example, foams), the quotient of the mass and the volume determined by the outer boundaries of the sample is determined as a ϱ density according to ASTM D 792. The true density can be determined by weighing the mass and determining the true volume.

With compact solids it is often sufficient to measure a single sample for the determination of the volume. With plastics in powder or granular form, the volume is determined by measuring the amount of displaced liquid in a pycnometer or by means of buoyancy measurements. In all cases one needs relatively accurate weighings, especially with small amounts of sample.

For many purposes it is simpler to use the flotation procedure in which the sample is made to float in a liquid of the same density. The density of the liquid may then be determined according to known methods with an aerometer. One can use aqueous zinc chloride or magnesium chloride solutions as the liquids. With densities below 1 g/cm^3, methanol-water mixtures are useful.

For density to be determined according to the flotation process, of course, the sample must not dissolve or swell in the liquid, and it must wet completely. Make sure that no air bubbles appear on the surface of the sample for they may affect the determination. Any bubbles must be completely removed. Carbon black, glass fibers, and other fillers can also influence the density measurements greatly. Foams cannot be characterized by density determinations.

If more accurate methods for the determination of the density are not available, immerse the sample in methanol (density, ϱ, at $20\,°C = 0.79$ g/cm^3), water ($\varrho = 1$ g/cm^3), saturated aqueous magnesium chloride solution ($\varrho = 1.34$ g/cm^3), or saturated aqueous zinc chloride solution ($\varrho = 2.01$ g/cm^3). Then observe whether the sample stays on the surface of the liquid, floats inside it, or sinks. Its behavior indicates whether it has a lower or a higher density than the liquid in which it is immersed. Table 8 contains the densities of the most important plastics (of course, there can be variations).

Table 8. Approximate Densities of Important Plastics

Density (g/cm^3)	Material
0.80	Silicone rubber (silica filled up to 1.25)
0.83	Polymethylpentene
0.85–0.92	Polypropylene
0.89–0.93	High-pressure (low-density) polyethylene
0.91–0.92	Polybutene-1
0.91–0.93	Polyisobutylene
0.92–1.0	Natural rubber
0.94–0.98	Low-pressure (high-density) polyethylene
1.01–1.04	Nylon 12
1.03–1.05	Nylon 11
1.04–1.06	Acrylonitrile-butadiene-styrene copolymers (ABS)
1.04–1.08	Polystyrene
1.05–1.07	Polyphenylene oxide
1.06–1.10	Styrene-acrylonitrile copolymers
1.07–1.09	Nylon 610
1.12–1.15	Nylon 6

Table 8. Approximate Densities of Important Plastics (continued)

Density (g/cm^3)	Material
1.13–1.16	Nylon 66
1.1 –1.4	Epoxy resins, unsaturated polyester resins
1.14–1.17	Polyacrylonitrile
1.15–1.25	Cellulose acetobutyrate
1.16–1.20	Polymethyl methacrylate
1.17–1.20	Polyvinyl acetate
1.18–1.24	Cellulose propionate
1.19–1.35	Plasticized PVC (approx. 40% plasticizer)
1.20–1.22	Polycarbonate (based on bisphenol A)
1.20–1.26	Crosslinked polyurethanes
1.26–1.28	Phenol-formaldehyde resins (unfilled)
1.21–1.31	Polyvinyl alcohol
1.25–1.35	Cellulose acetate
1.30–1.41	Phenol-formaldehyde resins filled with organic materials (paper, fabric)
1.3 –1.4	Polyvinyl fluoride
1.34–1.40	Celluloid
1.38–1.41	Polyethylene terephthalate
1.38–1.41	Rigid PVC
1.41–1.43	Polyoxymethylene (polyformaldehyde)
1.47–1.52	Urea- and melamine-formaldehyde resins with organic fillers
1.47–1.55	Chlorinated PVC
1.5 –2.0	Phenoplasts and aminoplasts with inorganic fillers
1.7 –1.8	Polyvinylidene fluoride
1.8 –2.3	Polyester and epoxy resins filled with glass fibers
1.86–1.88	Polyvinylidene chloride
2.1 –2.2	Polytrifluoromonochloroethylene
2.1 –2.3	Polytetrafluoroethylene

To prepare a saturated solution, add chemically pure zinc chloride or magnesium chloride in small portions and with shaking or stirring to distilled water until, on further addition, the material does not dissolve and a residue remains at the bottom. The solution process is relatively slow, and the saturated solutions are rather viscous.

For the preparation of a 1-liter saturated solution one needs approximately 1575 g zinc chloride or 475 g magnesium chloride. Both solutions are hygroscopic and therefore must be kept in closed flasks.

3.3   Behavior on Heating

Linear or branched, that is, not crosslinked, thermoplastic materials usually first begin to soften on heating and then on further heating (amorphous polymers) begin to flow over a rather ill-defined temperature range (see Fig. 3). Partially crystalline plastics in general have narrow melting ranges, which, however, are usually less sharply defined than the melting points of low molecular weight crystalline materials. Above the flow temperature the sample begins to break down chemically (pyrolysis). This process of thermal degradation produces low molecular weight fragments, which are often flammable or have a characteristic odor. Thermosets and elastomers show little or no flow up to their decomposition temperature (see Fig. 4). At that point they also form many typical degradation products, which give important information for the identification of plastic.

In addition to pyrolysis, flame tests yield useful information, since the behavior in the flame shows characteristic differences depending on the nature of the plastic. Pyrolysis tests and flame tests are therefore among the most important preliminary tests in the analysis of a plastic. They often permit direct conclusions so that one can then begin with specific tests.

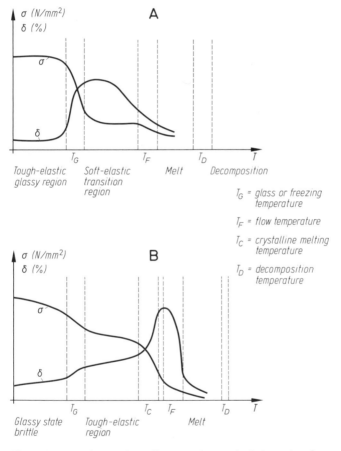

Figure 3. Dependence of tensile strength σ and of elongation δ on temperature for amorphous thermoplastics (A) and partially crystalline thermoplastics (B).

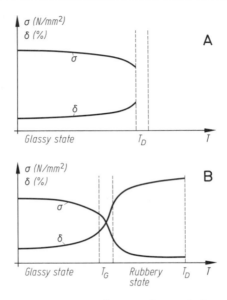

Figure 4. Dependence of tensile strength σ and elongation δ on temperature for thermosets (A) and for elastomers (B).

3.3.1   Pyrolysis Tests

To examine the behavior of a plastic on heating without direct exposure to flame, add a small sample to a pyrolysis tube, gripping the upper end of the tube with a clip or pair of tongs. At the open end of the tube place a piece of moist litmus or pH paper. In some cases one inserts a wad of loose cotton wool or glass wool that has been moistened with water or methanol in the open end of the pyrolysis tube. Heat the test tube in the flame of a Bunsen burner that has been reduced to minimum heat, taking care to point the open end of the tube away from the face. (*Caution:* Wear safety glasses.) Heating should occur so slowly that the changes in the sample and in the smell of the decomposition gases can be properly observed.

Depending on the reaction of the escaping vapors with litmus it is possible to distinguish three different

Table 9. Litmus and pH Tests for Vapors of Plastics*

Litmus Paper		
Red	Essentially unchanged	Blue
pH Paper		
0.5–4.0	5.0–5.5	8.0–9.5
Halogen-containing polymers	Polyolefins	Polyamides
Polyvinyl esters	Polyvinyl alcohol	ABS polymers
Cellulose esters	Polyvinyl acetals	Polyacrylonitrile
Polyethylene terephthalate	Polyvinyl ethers	Phenolic and cresol resins
Novolacs	Styrene polymers (included styrene-acrylonitrile copolymers)**	Amino resins (aniline-, melamine-, and urea-form-aldehyde resins
Polyurethane elastomers	Polymethacrylates	
Unsaturated polyester resins	Polyoxymethylene	
Fluorine-containing polymers	Polycarbonates	
Vulcanized fiber	Linear polyurethanes	
Polyalkylene sulfide	Silicones	
	Phenolic resins	
	Epoxy resins	
	Crosslinked polyurethanes	

 * Slowly heated in a pyrolysis tube.
** Some samples show slightly alkaline behavior.

groups: acidic (the litmus paper turns red), neutral (no color change), or basic (the litmus paper turns blue). The pH paper is somewhat more sensitive. Table 9 shows the reactions of the decomposition products of the most important plastics. Depending on their composition some plastics can appear in the pyrolysis test in different groups, for example, phenolformaldehyde resins or polyurethanes.

3.3.2   Flame Tests

To test the behavior of the plastic in a flame, hold a small sample of the plastic with a pair of tweezers or a spatula in a low flame. Reduce the gas supply to the Bunsen burner to its minimum. Observe the flammability of the plastic in and out of the flame. Also note the formation of drops of burning or melting plastic as well as the odor after the flame is extinguished. Table 10 shows the behavior of the most important plastics in the flame test. However, the flammability of plastics is influenced strongly by the addition of flame-retarding additives, and therefore in practice results may deviate from these shown in Table 10.

For a systematic evaluation of flammability and odor tests, the scheme described by G.H. Domsch (Kunststoffe 61 (1971), p.669) is recommended (see Figure 5, pages 52/53).

Table 10. Behavior of Plastics on Burning (Flame Test)

Flammability	Appearance of Flame	Odor of Vapors	Material
Does not burn	–	–	Silicones
	–	Stings (hydrofluoric acid, HF)	Polytetrafluoroethylene, polytrifluorochloroethylene
	–	–	Polyimides
Difficult to ignite, extinguishes when removed from flame	Bright, sooty	Phenol, formaldehyde	Phenolic resins
	Bright yellow	Ammonia, amines, formaldehyde	Amino resins
	Green edge	Hydrochloric acid	Chlorinated rubber, polyvinyl chloride, polyvinylidene chloride (without flammable plasticizers)
	Shiny, sooty	–	Polycarbonates
	Yellow, grey smoke	–	Silicone rubber
	Yellow-orange, blue smoke	Burnt horn	Polyamides

(continued)

Table 10. Behavior of Plastics on Burning (Flame Test) (continued)

Flammability	Appearance of Flame	Odor of Vapors	Material
Burns in the flame, extinguishes slowly or not at all outside the flame	Yellow	Phenol, burnt paper	Phenolic resin laminates
	Shiny, material decomposes	Irritating, scratches the throat	Polyvinyl alcohol
	Yellow-orange	Burnt rubber	Polychloroprene
	Yellow-orange, sooty	Sweetly aromatic	Polyethylene terephthalate
	Yellow, blue edge	Stinging (isocyanate)	Polyurethanes
	Yellow, blue center	Paraffin	Polyethylene, polypropylene
	Shiny, sooty	Sharp	Polyester resins (glass fiber reinforced)
	Yellow	Phenol	Epoxy resins (glass fiber reinforced)
Ignites readily, continues burning after flame is removed	Shiny, sooty	Sweetish, natural gas	Polystyrene

Dark yellow, slightly sooty	Acetic acid	Polyvinyl acetate
Dark yellow, sooty	Burnt rubber	Rubber
Shiny, blue center, crackles	Sweetish, fruity	Polymethyl methacrylate
Bluish	Formaldehyde	Polyoxymethylene
Dark yellow, slightly soft	Acetic acid and butyric acid	Cellulose acetobutyrate
Light green, sparks	Acetic acid	Cellulose acetate
Yellow-orange	Burnt paper	Cellulose
Bright, violent	Nitrogen oxides	Cellulose nitrate

Hold sample to the edge of the flame (if sample does not ignite at once,

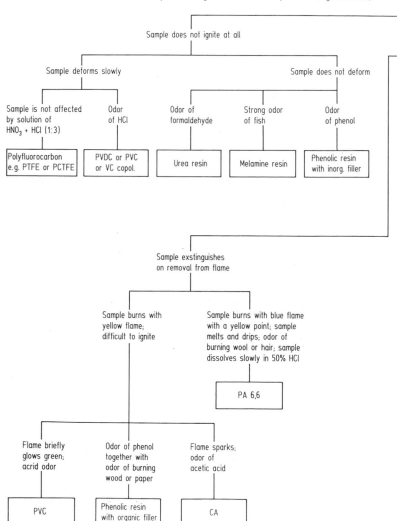

Figure 5. Flammability and Odor Tests (after G. H. Domsch)

hold the sample into the flame up to 10 s)

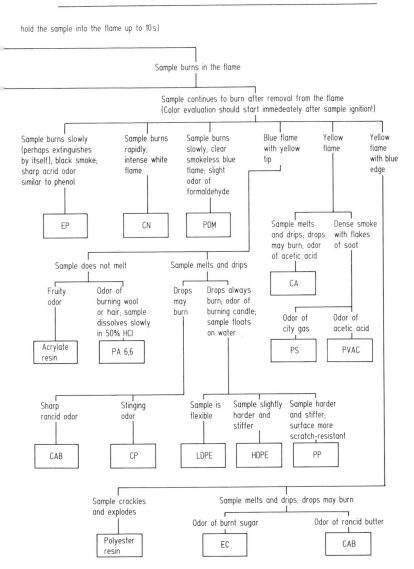

3.3.3   Melting Behavior

As was mentioned previously, softening or melting occurs only with linear plastics. In some cases, however, the softening or melting range lies above the range in which polymers are thermally stable. In that case, decomposition starts before melting of the sample can be observed. With crosslinked plastics there is usually no softening until just below the point where chemical degradation occurs. Therefore, this kind of behavior is an indication, although not an unequivocal one, that the material is a cured thermoset (see Fig. 4). In general, high molecular weight compounds do not have as sharp a melting point as crystalline low molecular weight organic compounds (see Fig. 3).

The glass or freezing temperatures of polymers are very characteristic of specific polymers. These are the temperatures at which certain molecular segments become mobile, without entire chains being able to glide past each other so that a viscous flow can begin. The determination of the glass temperature is hardly possible with simple means, because for many plastics it lies considerably below room temperature. Among the methods used are differential thermoanalysis, the measurement of temperature dependence of the refractive index, and mechanical properties such as the modulus of elasticity.

The softening range of a plastic can be determined with the usual methods of organic chemistry, either in a melting point tube or with a hot-stage microscope. A hot stage with which melting points can be determined to an accuracy of $2-3°K$ (see Fig. 6) is very useful. However, the resulting values often depend to a considerable extent on the rate of heating and on the presence of certain additives, especially plasticizers. The most reliable melting points ar those of partially crystalline polymers. The different polyamides, for example, can be easily distinguished (compare Section 6.2.10). Values for the most important plastics are shown in Table 11. A more comprehensive tabulation can be found in *Plastics Analysis Guide* by A. Krause, A. Lange, and M. Ezrin (Hanser Publishers, 1983).

Table 11. Softening and Melting Ranges
of Important Thermoplastics

Thermoplastic	Softening or Melting Range (°C)
Polyvinyl acetate	35– 85
Polystyrene	70–115
Polyvinyl chloride	75– 90 (softens)
Polyethylene, density 0.92 g/cm³	about 110
density 0.94 g/cm³	about 120
density 0.96 g/cm³	about 130
Polybutene-1	125–135
Polyvinylidene chloride	115–140 (softens)
Polymethyl methacrylate	120–160
Cellulose acetate	125–175
Polyacrylonitrile	130–150 (softens)
Polyoxymethylene	165–185
Polypropylene	160–170
Nylon 12	170–180
Nylon 11	180–190
Polytrifluorochloroethylene	200–220
Nylon 6,10	210–220
Nylon 6	215–225
Polybutylene terephthalate	220
Polycarbonate	220–230
Poly-4-methylpentene-1	240
Nylon 6,6	250–260
Polyethylene terephthalate	250–260

Figure 6. Hot stage. A linear temperature gradient from 50 to 250 °C is created by resistance heaters along the metal bar. The sample (as finely divided as possible) is placed directly on the metal bar. The temperature at the border between solid powder and molten material can be determined directly from a scale on the hot stage.

4 Testing for Heteroatoms

The previously described simple preliminary tests are not always sufficient to identify an unknown plastic with certainty. In some cases the use of chemical reactions for identification purposes cannot be avoided. First one tests for heteroatoms, those elements which are present in the plastic in addition to carbon and hydrogen, such as nitrogen, sulfur, chlorine, fluorine, silicon, and sometimes phosphorus. Unfortunately, there is no simple direct method for the certain identification of oxygen, so it is not possible to test for oxygen in a qualitative manner. The following reactions presuppose a certain amount of experimental skill.

For the qualitative determination of the elements nitrogen, sulfur, and chlorine, the *Lassaigne method* is usually used. Combine approximately 50–100 mg of a finely divided sample with a pea-sized piece of sodium or potassium in a pyrolysis tube. Heat this carefully in a Bunsen flame until the metal melts. (*Caution!* Wear safety glasses and keep the opening of the tube directed away from the eyes.) The sample must be free of water, which would react explosively with the metal. Sodium and potassium must be stored in oil or immersed in a similar inert hydrocarbon. When used, hold the required amount with tweezers and cut it with a knife or a spatula on a piece of filter paper. Then carefully blot it dry with the filter paper. Use it immediately and return the remainder to the oil-containing bottle. In no case should the remainder be destroyed by throwing it into water.

Carefully place the glowing tube in a small beaker with approximately 10 ml distilled water. The glass tube will shatter and the reaction products will dissolve in the water. Unreacted metal will react with the water; therefore, carefully stir with a glass rod until no further reaction occurs. Then filter the nearly colorless liquid or remove the liquid by careful pipetting from the glass splinters and carbonized residues. For the following tests, use approximately 1–2 ml of this original solution.

- *Nitrogen.* Add a small amount (a spatula tip) of ferrous sulfate to a 1–2 ml sample of the original solution and boil it quickly. Let it cool and add a few drops of 1.5% ferric chloride solution. After acidification with dilute hydrochloric acid, a precipitate of Berlin blue occurs. The presence of a small amount of nitrogen results in a light green solution from which a precipitate results only after standing for several hours. If the solution remains yellow, there is no nitrogen present.
- *Sulfur.* The original solution is reacted with an approximately 1% aqueous sodium nitroferricyanide solution. A deep violet color indicates sulfur. This reaction is very sensitive; to confirm, add a drop of the alkaline solution of the sample under investigation to a silver coin. If sulfur is present, a brown spot of silver sulfide will form. An alternative procedure is to acidify the original solution with acetic acid (test with litmus or pH paper) and then add several drops of aqueous 2 M lead acetate solution or test with lead acetate paper. A black precipitate of lead sulfide or darkening of the paper indicates sulfur.

The presence of sulfur in polysulfides, polysulfones and in sulfur-vulcanized rubber can be demonstrated by the following somewhat uncertain test. The sample is heated in dry air (pyrolysis) and the gases formed during this process are bubbled through a dilute barium chloride solution. The presence of sulfur is indicated by a white precipitate of barium sulfate.

● *Chlorine.* This is a general test for heavier halogens, but bromine and iodine almost never occur in plastics. Acidify a sample of the original solution with dilute nitric acid and add a small amount of silver nitrate solution (2 g in 100 ml distilled water; keep the solution in the dark or in a brown flask). A white flaky precipitate that dissolves again in the addition of an excess of ammonia indicates the presence of chlorine. A light yellow precipitate that is difficult to dissolve in ammonia indicates the presence of bromine. A yellow precipitate that is insoluble in ammonia is characteristic for iodine.

● *Fluorine.* Acidify the original solution with dilute hydrochloric acid or acetic acid and then add a 1 N calcium chloride solution. A gel-like precipitate of calcium fluoride indicates the presence of fluorine (compare also below).

● *Phosphorus.* On the addition of a solution of ammonium molybdate to a portion of the original solution that was acidified with nitric acid, one obtains a precipitate on heating for approximately 1 min. To prepare the molybdate solution, dissolve 30 g ammonium molybdate in approximately 60 ml hot water, cool, and add water to make 100 ml. Then add a thin stream of a solution of 10 g ammonium sulfate in 100 ml 55% nitric acid (from 16 ml water and 84 ml concentrated nitric acid). Let it stand for 24 hr, remove the supernatant by suction or by decantation, and keep the solution well sealed in the dark.

● *Silicon.* Mix approximately 30–50 mg of the plastic sample with 100 mg dry sodium carbonate and 10 mg sodium peroxide in a small platinum or nickel crucible (carefully). Melt it slowly over a flame. After cooling, dissolve the material in a few drops of water, bring it quickly to a boil, and neutralize or slightly acidify it with dilute nitric acid. Add 1 drop of molybdate solution (see phosphorus test), then heat nearly to boiling. Cool the sample, add 1 drop of benzidine solution (50 mg benzidine dissolved in 10 ml 50% acetic acid; add water to make 100 ml), and then add 1 drop of saturated aqueous sodium acetate solution. A blue color indicates silicon.

Other Identification Reactions

Halogens, especially chlorine, can be easily identified with the very sensitive *Beilstein test.* Heat the end of a copper wire in a Bunsen flame until the flame is colorless. After cooling, put a small amount of the substance to be examined on the wire and heat it at the edge of the colorless part of the flame. When the plastic burns, the presence of halogen can be inferred if the flame is colored green or blue-green.

Fluorine can be demonstrated by placing approximately 0.5 g of the plastic in a small test tube and pyrolyzing it in a Bunsen flame. After cooling, add a few milliliters of concentrated sulfuric acid. The presence of fluorine is indicated by a characteristic non-wettability of the wall of the test tube. (Make a comparison experiment with a sample of known fluorine content.)

From the results of the tests for heteroatoms, useful conclusions can be drawn:

- *Chlorine* occurs in plastics such as PVC, chlorinated polyethylene, and rubber hydrochloride. Some plasticizers also contain chlorine. Flameproofing agents often contain chlorine or bromine.

- *Nitrogen* is found in polyamides, aminoplastics, cellulose nitrate, and in films treated with nitrogen-containing lacquers.

- *Sulfur,* when found in rubber elastic materials, indicates vulcanized rubber, polysulfones, or polysulfides.

- *Phosphorus* is seldom found in plastics (with the exception of casein). However, it indicates the presence of phosphate plasticizers, stabilizers, or flameproofing agents.

A compilation of the most important plastics containing heteroatoms is shown in Table 12.

Table 12. Classification* of Plastics by their Heteroatoms

	–	O			Halogens	N, O	S, O	Si	N, S	N, S, P
		Cannot be saponified	Can be saponified**							
			SN < 200	SN > 200						
Polyolefins		Polyvinyl alcohol	Natural resins	Polyvinyl acetate and copolymers	Polyvinyl chloride	Polyamides	Polyalkylene sulfide	Silicones	Thiourea condensates	Casein resins
Polystyrene		Polyvinyl ethers	Modified phenolic resins	Poly-acrylates and polymeth-acrylates	Polyvinylidene chloride and copolymers	Poly-urethanes Polyureas	Vulcanized rubbers	Polysiloxanes	Sulfamide condensates	
Poly-isoprene		Polyvinyl acetals		Polyesters	Polyfluoro-hydrocarbons	Amino-plastics				
Butyl rubber		Polyglycols		Alkyd resins	Chlorinated rubber	Polyacrylo-nitrile and copolymers				
		Poly-aldehydes		Cellulose esters	Rubber hydro-chloride	Polyvinyl-carbazole				
		Phenolic resins				Polyvinyl-pyrrolidone				
		Xylene resins								
		Cellulose								
		Cellulose ethers								

* After W. Kupfer Z. analyt. Chem. 192, 219 (1963).   ** SN = Saponification number.

5 Analytical Procedures

On the basis of the preliminary tests described in previous chapters and with the use of certain specific reactions, the most important plastics can be identified through simple separation procedures. Test for heteroatoms (Chapter 4), then for solubility in different solvents (Section 3.1). If necessary, test for other characteristic physical properties of chemical reactions.

As has previously been pointed out, the solubility of plastics depends in many cases on the molecular weight. With copolymers and polymer mixtures it also depends on the composition, and this can lead to problems. In that case, it is necessary to use additional, more complicated tests.

Plastics can be classified into four groups according to the elements present. Group I contains chlorine or fluorine, group II contains nitrogen, group III contains sulfur, and group IV contains no identifiable heteroatoms.

For the following solubility determination (procedure given in Section 3.1), use a fresh sample of the unknown. On heating the solvent, remember that many organic liquids or their vapors are flammable!

5.1   Analysis by Groups

Group I   Chlorine- and Fluorine-Containing Plastics

Heat the sample in a test tube with an approximately 50% solution of sulfuric acid. An odor of acetic acid indicates copolymers of vinyl chloride and vinyl acetate.

If the result is negative, follow the procedure in Section 6.2.7 for behavior toward pyridine. The process of distinguishing plastics in this group on the basis of their solubility is long and the results are usually uncertain. In this group one also tests for fluorine-containing plastics, especially polytetrafluoroethylene and polytrifluorochloroethylene. No simple specific reaction is known for these materials. For the identification in addition to their high density of 2.1–2.3 g/cm^3 and their complete insolubility at room temperature, one can use the presence of fluorine. The key to identification of polytrifluorochloroethylene is the simultaneous positive result of a chlorine test. Polyvinyl fluoride and fluorine-containing elastomers are found less frequently, and it is not possible to identify them with simple tests.

Group II   Nitrogen-Containing Plastics

Diphenylamine test: Suspend 0.1 g diphenylamine in 30 ml water and then add carefully 100 ml concentrated sulfuric acid. (*Note:* The acid should be added slowly.) Add a drop of the fresh reagent to the plastic sample on a plate; a dark blue coloration indicates cellulose nitrate.

If the result is negative, test for bound formaldehyde. Heat a small sample of the plastic with 2 ml concentrated sulfuric acid and a few crystals of chromotropic acid for 10 min at 60–70 °C. A deep violet coloration indicates formaldehyde. Cellulose nitrate, polyvinyl acetate, polyvinylbutyral, and cellulose acetate give a red coloration; these materials, however, are not included in this part of the analytical procedure.

If the formaldehyde test is positive, heat a sample of the plastic with a 10% glycolic solution of potassium hydroxide (dissolve 10 g KOH in approximately 95 ml ethylene glycol). A smell of ammonia (confirm with moist red litmus paper) indicates urea resins. Melamine resins do not liberate ammonia. However, they can be identified by the thiosulfate reaction and clearly distinguished from urea resins. For this purpose, heat a small amount of the sample in a test tube with a few drops of concentrated hydrochloric acid in an oil bath to 190–200 °C until congo red paper no longer turns blue. Cool the solution and add a few crystals of sodium thiosulfate. Cover the tube with a piece of congo red paper that has been moistened with 3% hydrogen peroxide, and heat in the bath to 160 °C. A blue color indicates melamine.

Thiourea resins are identified by the simultaneous presence of nitrogen and sulfur. (For identification of the individual elements, see Section 6.2.13.)

If the formaldehyde test is negative, cover a sample with nonaqueous sodium carbonate in a test tube and heat the tube until the material melts. The odor of ammonia indicates polyamides. If the vapors are acrid and neutral or lightly acidic to pH paper (sometimes also basic), this indicates urethanes. A sweet odor indicates polyacrylonitrile. Such vapors are clearly basic.

(Test, see Section 6.2.4.) Group II tests are sum-
marized in Fig. 7.

Group III   Sulfur-Containing Polymers

In addition to polyalkylene sulfides, thiourea resins,
and thiochlorinated polyethylene, this group includes
sulfur-vulcanized natural and synthetic elastomers.
Due to their rubberlike behavior, they will be discussed together with the identification reactions of elastomers in Section 6.2.18. Polysulfones, which are used
as engineering plastics, should also be considered in
this group. The thioureas have not been identified in
group II, because of the simultaneous presence of
nitrogen.

Polyalkylene sulfides (thioplastics) have a relatively
high density ($1.3-1.6$ g/cm^3) and usually have a strong
odor of hydrogen sulfide or mercaptans (like rotten
eggs). The odor is especially strong on heating, and in
this way they can be qualitatively identified.

Group IV   Plastics without Heteroatoms

The large groups of plastics without heteroatoms can
only be incompletely identified with this separation
procedure. Place the sample in water. If it dissolves
slowly, then it may be polyvinyl alcohol. (For specific
identification, see Section 6.2.6.) If the plastic is insoluble in water, then check first for formaldehyde (Section 6.1.4). The only positive reaction in this group is
given by phenol formaldehyde resins and polyformal-
dehydes (polyoxymethylene).

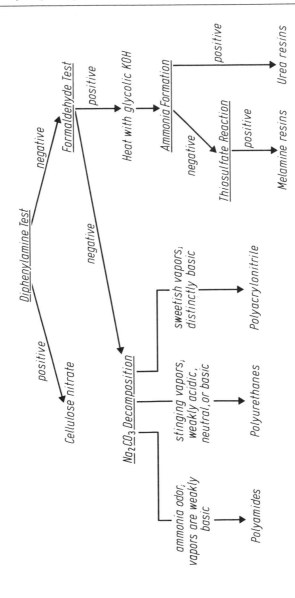

Figure 7. Tests for group II, nitrogen-containing plastics.

Next, test for phenols (see Section 6.1.3). They may result from phenol and cresol formaldehyde resins and also from epoxy resins or polycarbonates based on bisphenol A.

A further test for acetate (Section 6.2.5) makes it possible to identify polymers containing vinyl acetate as well as cellulose acetate or cellulose acetate butyrate (6.2.16).

These tests, however, do not identify certain chemically very inert plastics such as polyethylene, polypropylene, polyisobutylene, polystyrene, polymethyl methacrylate, polyacrylates, polyethylene terephthalate, natural rubber, butadiene rubber, polyisoprene, and silicones. Their identification requires specific individual reactions, described in Chapter 6.

It is relatively simple to separate and characterize mixtures of polyvinylchloride, polyethylene and polystyrene which constitute a major part of all solid plastics waste. The procedure is as follows:

2 g of the mixture is stirred for 1 hour at room temperature in toluene. The insoluble residue is removed by filtration and dried at 80 °C (if possible in a drying closet). The filtrate contains polystyrene which can be separated from the solvent either by carefully evaporating the toluene, or by slowly adding the solution dropwise to about 300 ml methanol in order to precipitate the polystyrene. In order to confirm that the material is polystyrene, use the specific identification test for polystyrene described in Section 6.2.2. After separation of the polystyrene, the previously dried solid residue is treated with ca. 50 ml toluene for about 30 minutes at 80 °C on a waterbath. This treatment dissolves the polyethylene almost completely, whereas polyvinylchloride remains insoluble under these conditions. The contents of the flask are

filtered while still hot and the solid residue is washed with heated toluene and then dried for an hour at 50°C. To identify the material see Section 6.2.7. The polyethylene which was dissolved in the hot toluene precipitates on cooling of the solution to room temperature. It can be recovered by filtration and identified according to the procedure given in Section 6.2.1.

An extensive compilation of physical properties, solubilities, pyrolysis behavior and some characteristic identifications of individual plastics are contained in the Plastics Identification Table of Hj. Saechtling which forms a part of this book and can be found in the pocket on the inside of the back cover.

6 Specific Identification Tests

6.1 General Identification Reactions

6.1.1 Liebermann-Storch-Morawski Reaction

Dissolve or suspend a few milligrams of the sample in 2 ml hot acetic anhydride. After cooling, add 3 drops of 50% sulfuric acid (from equal volumes of water and concentrated sulfuric acid). Watch the color reaction immediately and again after the sample has stood for 10 min. Heat it to 100°C, using a water bath. This test is not specific but is often quite useful as an indicator.

Table 13. Color Changes in the L-S-M Reaction

Material	Immediate	Color after 10 min	After Heating to about 100°C
Phenolic resins	Reddish violet-pink	Brown	Brown-red
Polyvinyl alcohol	Colorless-yellowish	Colorless-yellowish	Brown-black
Polyvinyl acetate	Colorless-yellowish	Blue grey	Brown-black
Chlorinated rubber	Yellow brown	Yellow brown	Reddish yellow brown
Epoxy resins	Colorless to yellow	Colorless to yellow	Colorless to yellow
Polyurethanes	Lemon yellow	Lemon yellow	Brown, green fluorescence

6.1.2   Color Reaction with *p*-Dimethyl-aminobenzaldehyde

Heat 0.1–0.2 g of the sample in a test tube, and place the pyrolyzed product on a bare cotton plug. Drop the cotton in a 14% methanol solution of *para*-dimethyl-aminobenzaldehyde with a drop of concentrated hydrochloric acid. If polycarbonates are present, a deep blue color is produced. Polyamides show a bordeaux red color.

6.1.3   The Gibbs Indophenol Test

The Gibbs indophenol test is useful for the identification of phenol in phenolic resins and in substances that split off phenol or phenol derivatives on heating. Polycarbonates or epoxy resins are examples of this. Heat a small sample for a maximum of 1 min in a pyrolysis tube and cover the opening of the tube with a piece of prepared filter paper. To prepare the paper, drench it in a saturated ether solution of 2,6-dibromoquinone-4-chlorimide and then air-dry it. After the pyrolysis, hold the paper over ammonia vapor or moisten it with 1–2 drops of dilute ammonia. A blue color indicates phenol (cresol, xylenol).

6.1.4   Formaldehyde Test

Heat a small sample of the plastic with 2 ml concentrated sulfuric acid and a few crystals of chromotropic acid for about 10 min at 60–70°C. A strong violet color indicates formaldehyde. Cellulose acetate, cellulose nitrate, polyvinyl acetate, or polyvinylbutyral will yield a red color.

6.2   Specific Plastics

6.2.1   Polyolefins

Polyethylene and polypropylene are the polyolefins most commonly used as plastics. Polybutene-1 and poly-4-methylpentene-1 are less common. Also important are certain copolymers of ethylene and polyisobutylene, which is used for gaskets. The simplest method of identification of these materials is by infrared spectroscopy. However, some information can also be obtained from the melting range (see also Section 3.3.3):

Polyethylene (depending on density)	105–135 °C
Polypropylene	160–170 °C
Polybutene-1	120–135 °C
Poly-4-methylpentene-1	above 240 °C

A first indication that polyolefins are present can be obtained from a simple density measurement. Contrary to the behavior of other plastics, the polyolefins float on water. The only other plastics that float on water are foamed plastics or those containing foaming agents.

The reaction of the pyrolysis vapors with mercury(II) oxide will differentiate between these materials. To do this, heat a dry sample of the plastic in the pyrolysis tube closed with a piece of prepared filter paper. To prepare the paper, drench it with a solution of 0.5 g yellow mercury(II) oxide in sulfuric acid (1.5 ml concentrated sulfuric acid added to 8 ml water, carefully). If the vapor gives a golden yellow spot, this indicates polyisobutylene, butyl rubber, and polypropylene (the latter only after a few minutes). Polyethylene does not react. Natural and nitrile rubber, as well as polybutadiene, yield a brown spot. Waxlike greases are the products in the pyrolysis of polyethylene and polypropylene. Polyethylene smells like paraffin, and polypropylene is slightly aromatic.

Polyethylene and polypropylene may also be differentiated by scratching the sample with your fingernail: whereas polyethylene will show scratch marks, polypropylene is scratch resistant.

6.2.2   Polystyrene

When polystyrene is heated in a dry test tube styrene monomer is formed which is easily identified by its typical odor.

Polystyrene and most styrene-containing copolymers can be identified by placing a small sample in a small test tube, adding 4 drops of fuming nitric acid, and evaporating the acid without having the polymer decompose. The residue is then heated over a small flame for approximately 1 min. Fasten the test tube with its open end tilted slightly down and covered with a piece of filter paper. Prepare the paper by drenching it in a concentrated solution of 2,6-dibromoquinone-4-chlorimide in ether and then drying it in air. On moistening with a drop of dilute ammonia, the paper turns blue if polystyrene is present. If the sample still contains some free nitric acid, the test is affected and the paper turns brown, which may conceal the blue color. This identification is also useful for styrene-butadiene copolymers as well as for ABS (acrylonitrile-butadiene-styrene copolymers). The presence of acrylonitrile can be confirmed by a test for nitrogen.

6.2.3   Polymethyl methacrylate

Polymethyl methacrylate plays an important role
among the acrylates as an injection molding material
as well as a glasslike material. For its identification,
0.5 g sample is heated in a test tube with approximately
0.5 g dry sand. On depolymerization, monomeric
methyl methacrylate is obtained. This is captured at
the opening of the test tube on a glass fiber plug. The
methyl methacrylate monomer may be distilled from
one test tube into another through a bent piece of glass
tubing passing through a rubber stopper (Fig. 8). Heat
a sample of the monomer with a small amount of concentrated nitric acid (density 1,4 g/cm^3) until a clear
yellow solution is obtained. After cooling, dilute with
approximately half its volume of water, then add a
5–10% sodium nitrite solution dropwise. Methyl

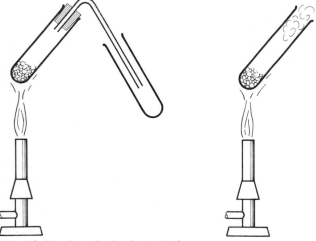

Figure 8. Depolymerization in a test tube.

methacrylate, which may be extracted with chloroform, is indicated by a blue-green color.

On pyrolysis, polyacrylates yield, in addition to monomeric esters, several strong-smelling decomposition products. The pyrolysates are either yellow or brown and acidic.

6.2.4   Polyacrylonitrile

Polyacrylonitrile is most often encountered as a fiber. It is also found in acrylonitrile-containing plastics copolymerized with styrene, butadiene, or methyl methacrylate. All such polymers contain nitrogen.

To identify acrylonitrile polymers, take a sample of the material and add a small amount of zinc dust and a few drops of 25% sulfuric acid (1 ml concentrated sulfuric acid added to 3 ml water, slowly). Heat this mixture in a porcelain crucible. Cover the crucible with filter paper moistened with the following reagent solution: Dissolve 2.86 g copper acetate in 1.0 liter water. Then dissolve 14 g benzidine in 100 ml acetic acid, and to 67.5 ml of this solution add 52.5 ml of water. Keep both the copper acetate and benzidine solutions in separate containers in the dark. Mix them in equal volumes just before use. The presence of acrylonitrile is indicated by a bluish spot on the filter paper.

The presence of acrylonitrile in copolymers can also be demonstrated by heating a sample of the dry material in a test tube and testing with indicator paper for the formation of HCN. Prepare the indicator paper by dissolving 0.3 g copper(II) acetate in 100 ml water. Impregnate strips of filter paper, then air-dry them. Just before use, dip the strips in a solution of 0.05 g benzidine in 100 ml 1 N acetic acid (prepared from

equal parts of 2 *N* acetic acid and water). If HCN
passes over the moist paper, the paper turns blue.

When polyacrylonitrile is pyrolyzed, hydrogen
cyanide (HCN) is formed and may be identified by
means of the Prussian Blue reaction. 0.5 g of the polyacrylonitrile sample is completely pyrolyzed in a test
tube and the pyrolysis vapors are introduced into 3 ml
of dilute sodium hydroxide solution. After addition of
about 1 ml ferrous sulfate solution, the mixture is
brought to a boil and then reacted with a few drops of
ferric chloride solution. After acidification with dilute
hydrochloric acid, nitrile group containing polymers
give rise to a characteristic blue color.

To distinguish between polyacrylonitrile and polyamides or polyurethanes, one dissolves a few mg of the
sample in about 3 ml of dimethylformamide. After
addition of about 3 ml of 60% sodium hydroxide solution (carefully dissolve about 6 g NaOH in 10 ml
water), the mixture is heated. An orange-red coloration is observed only if polyacrylonitrile is present.

6.2.5   Polyvinyl acetate

Polymers containing vinyl acetate can be recognized by
the fact that they produce acetic acid on thermal
decomposition. Cellulose acetate behaves in a similar
fashion. To test this, pyrolyze a small amount of sample and catch the vapors on water-moistened cotton.
Then wash the cotton and collect the liquid in a test
tube. Add 3–4 drops of a 5% aqueous lanthanum
nitrate solution, 1 drop 0.1 *N* iodine solution, and 1–2
drops concentrated ammonia. Polyvinyl acetate
becomes deeply blue or almost black. Polyacrylate
becomes reddish, polyvinyl acetate green to blue. As a

further test, use the Liebermann-Storch-Morawski reaction (see 6.1.1). Polyvinyl acetate gives a purple-brown color on wetting with 0.01 N iodinepotassium iodate solution (0.1 N solution diluted to 10 times its volume). This color becomes stronger on washing with water.

6.2.6   Polyvinyl alcohol

Saponification of polyvinyl acetate gives polyvinyl alcohol. The latter has no particular importance as a plastic raw material. The identification reactions will yield different results depending on the conversion during saponification. Highly saponified polyvinyl alcohols are insoluble in organic solvents but soluble in water and formamide. For the test involving the reaction with iodine, react 5 ml of the aqueous solution of polyvinyl alcohol with 2 drops of 0.1 N iodine-potassium iodide solution. Dilute this with water until the resulting color is only just recognizable. React 5 ml of this solution with as much borax as will fit on the tip of a spatula. Shake this and acidify it with 5 ml of concentrated hydrochloric acid. A strong green color, especially on the undissolved borax grains, indicates polyvinyl alcohol. The presence of starch and dextrin can interfere with this test.

6.2.7   Polymers containing Chlorine

In addition to polyvinyl chloride (PVC), the chlorine-containing polymers and different copolymers of vinyl chloride are: polyvinylidene chloride, chloro-rubber, rubber hydrochloride, chlorinated polyolefins, polychloroprene, and polytrifluorochloroethylene. In addition to detecting chlorine with the Beilstein test (see Chapter 4), these polymers can be identified by using the color reaction with pyridine (see Table 14).

First the material must be freed of plasticizers by extraction with ether. Alternatively, dissolve the sample in tetrahydrofuran, filter off possible undissolved components, and reprecipitate it by adding methanol. After extraction and drying at a maximum of 75°C, react a small sample with 1 ml pyridine. Let it stand for a few minutes, then add 2–3 drops of a 5% methanolic sodium hydroxide solution (1 g sodium hydroxide dissolved in 20 ml methanol). Note the color immediately, after 5 min, and again after 1 hr. For a more definitive test, boil a small amount of plasticizer-free material for 1 min with 1 ml pyridine. Divide the solution into two parts. Boil both portions again and then immediately add 2 drops of 5% methanolic sodium hydroxide to one. Cool the other portion and then add to it 2 drops of methanolic sodium hydroxide. Observe the color immediately and after 5 min. (See Table 14.)

6.2.8 Polyoxymethylene

Polyoxymethylenes (polymers of formaldehyde or trioxane) produce formaldehyde on heating. The chromotropic acid test for formaldehyde is positive (see Section 6.1.4).

6.2.9 Polycarbonates

Almost all polycarbonates used in plastics contain bisphenol A. For positive identification, the color reac-

Table 14. Color Reactions of Chlorine-Containing Plastics on Treating with Pyridine

Material	Boiled with Pyridine and Reagent Solution		Boiled with Pyridine; Cooled; Reagent Solution Added		Pyridine and Reagent Solution Added to Sample without Heating	
	Immediate	After 5 min	Immediate	After 5 min	Immediate	After 5 min
Polyvinyl chloride	Red-brown	Blood red, brown-red	Blood red, brown-red	Red-brown, black precipitate	Red-brown	Black-brown
Chlorinated PVC	Blood red brown-red	Brown-red	Brown-red	Red-brown, black precipitate	Red-brown	Red-brown
Chlorinated rubber	Dark red-brown	Dark red-brown	Black-brown	Black-brown precipitate	Olive-brown	Olive-brown
Polychloroprene	White-cloudy	White-cloudy	Colorless	Colorless	White-cloudy	White-cloudy
Polyvinylidene chloride	Brown-black	Brown-black precipitate	Brown-black precipitate	Black-brown precipitate	Brown-black	Brown-black
PVC molding compound	Yellow	Brown-black precipitate	White-cloudy	White precipitate	Colorless	Colorless

tion with p-dimethylaminobenzaldehyde (see Section 6.1.2) or the Gibbs indophenol test (see Section 6.1.3) are used.

Polycarbonates are completely saponified in a few minutes on heating in 10% alcoholic potassium hydroxide. Potassium carbonate precipitates during this reaction and can be filtered off. Acidify the precipitate with dilute sulfuric acid, which will release carbon dioxide. On passing the gas into a barium hydroxide solution a white precipitate of barium carbonate forms.

6.2.10   Polyamides

The most important industrial polyamides are nylons 6, 66, 610, 11, and 12. There are also a number of different copolymer amides that can be identified with simple means as polyamides (for example through the odor of burnt horn on exposure to a flame; see Section 3.3.2). However, complete identification is not always possible.

In some cases the melting point determination permits the distinction between the different polyamides:

Polyamide Type	Melting Point Range (°C)
Nylon 6	215–225
Nylon 66	250–260
Nylon 610	210–220
Nylon 11	180–190
Nylon 12	170–180

Polyamides can also be recognized through the color reaction with p-dimethylaminobenzaldehyde (see Section 6.1.2).

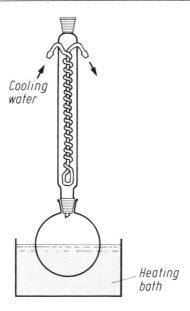

Figure 9. Heating and boiling using reflux condenser.

Polyamides can be readily identified by the acids formed on acid hydrolysis of the respective polyamides. For this purpose, heat 5 g of the sample with 50 ml concentrated hydrochloric acid using a reflux condenser (Fig. 9). Continue reflux until the major part of the sample has dissolved. Then boil the solution with charcoal until the color disappears and filter it while it is hot. After cooling, filter off the precipitated acids and recrystallize them from a small amount of water. If no acids precipitate, extract the filtrate with ether. Evaporate the ether and recrystallize the residue from water. The acids have the following melting points:

Adipic acid (nylon 66)	152 °C
Sebacic acid (nylon 610)	133 °C
ε-Aminocaproic acid hydrochloride (nylon 6)	123 °C
11-Aminoundecanoic acid (nylon 11)	145 °C
12-Aminolauric acid (nylon 12)	163 °C

Polyamides are easily differentiated from polyacrylonitrile by dissolution of the sample in dimethylformamide and subsequent addition of sodium hydroxide solution (see Section 6.2.4).

6.2.11 Polyurethanes

On pyrolysis, polyurethanes reform the isocyanates used in their synthesis to some extent. For their identification, heat a dry sample in a test tube, pass the resulting vapors over filter paper, and then moisten the filter paper with a 1% methanolic solution of 4-nitrobenzodiazoniumfluoroborate solution (Nitrazol CF extra, Hoechst AG). Depending on the type of isocyanate, the paper will turn yellow, reddish brown, or violet.

To distinguish between polyurethanes and polyacrylonitrile see Section 6.2.4.

6.2.12 Phenolics

Phenolic resins are made from phenol or phenol derivatives and formaldehyde. In many cases they also contain inorganic or organic fillers. After curing, the resins are insoluble in all the usual solvents, but they dissolve with decomposition in benzylamine. Phenolic resins may be identified in the Gibbs indophenol test (see Section 6.1.3). The bound formaldehyde may be identified with chromotropic acid (see Section 6.1.4).

6.2.13   Aminoplastics

The aminoplastics are condensation products of formaldehyde and urea, thiourea, melamine, or aniline. They are often filled with finely ground wood, stone, or asbestos, etc., and are used mainly as molded parts or laminates. All aminoplastics contain nitrogen and bound formaldehyde, which can be identified using chromotropic acid (see Section 6.1.4).

A specific identification test for urea is the enzymatic reaction with urease. 50 mg of powdered resin, that is, 0.1 ml of the resin solution in a test tube, is carefully heated with a Bunsen burner until all formaldehyde has been removed (check odor!). After cooling and neutralizing with 10% sodium hydroxide using phenolphthalein as indicator, 1 drop of 1 N sulfuric acid and 0.2 ml of a freshly prepared 10% urease solution are added. A moist piece of litmus paper is then attached to the upper rim of the test tube. After a short time the blue coloration of the indicator paper demonstrates the presence of ammonia which is formed only by urea-containing resins and not by melamine resins. Hexamethylene tetramine is the only substance that may interfere with this reaction.

Urea and thiourea resins can be identified by taking a few milligrams of the sample, adding 1 drop of hot concentrated hydrochloric acid (about 110°C), and heating until dry. After cooling, add 1 drop of phenylhydrazine and heat the sample for 5 min in an oil bath at 195°C. Cool it and add 3 drops of dilute ammonia (1:1) and 5 drops of a 10% aqueous nickel sulfate solution.

On shaking with chloroform, the solution becomes red to violet indicating the presence of urea or thiourea.

An additional test for sulfur (see Chapter 4) permits a distinction between urea and thiourea. Melamine resins can be recognized by pyrolysis. Heat a small sample with a few drops of concentrated hydrochloric acid. Use a pyrolysis tube and an oil bath at 190–200°C. Cover the tube with congo red paper, heat it until the paper no longer turns blue, and cool. Then add a few crystals of sodium thiosulfate to the cooled residue. Cover the pyrolysis tube with congo red paper moistened with a 3% hydrogen peroxide solution and heat it in the oil bath at 160°C. In the presence of melamine, the paper becomes blue (urea resins do not react).

Aniline resins may be identified by pyrolytic decomposition. The addition of the gases produced to either sodium hypochlorite or calcium hypochlorite solution yields a red-violet or violet solution.

6.2.14   Epoxy Resins

There are no simple specific tests for the unconverted epoxy groups or the crosslinked units in hardened epoxy resins. Epoxy resins give a positive reaction for phenol according to the Gibbs indophenol test (see Section 6.1.4) (due to the presence of bisphenol A). In contrast to the phenolic resins, however, the formaldehyde test with chromotropic acid (see Section 6.1.4) is negative. All epoxy resins produce acetaldehyde during pyrolysis below 250°C. Heat a sample of the material in a pyrolysis tube in an oil bath to 240°C. Pass the vapors onto filter paper which has been moistened with a fresh aqueous solution of 5% sodium nitroprussate and morpholine. A blue color indicates an epoxy resin.

An epoxy resin may also be recognized in the following way: Dissolve approximately 100 mg resin at room temperature in about 10 ml concentrated sulfuric acid. Then add about 1 ml concentrated nitric acid. After 5 min, top the solution carefully with 5% aqueous sodium hydroxide. In the presence of epoxy resins based on bisphenol A a cherry-red color will appear at the interface of the layers.

6.2.15 Polyesters

Unsaturated polyesters are produced in the form of dissolved resins in polymerizable monomers (usually styrene). They are also known in the form of molding resins or as hardened products. One should distinguish between them and the saturated aliphatic and aromatic polyesters. Among the latter are polyethylene terephthalate and polybutylene terephthalate.

The acidic components of most unsaturated polyesters are maleic, phthalic, sebacic, fumaric, or adipic acid. All of these can be directly identified.

Phthalic acid: Heat a small sample of the polymer with thymol (1 part sample to 3 parts thymol) and 5 drops of concentrated sulfuric acid for 10 min at 120–150°C. After cooling, dissolve the sample in 50% ethanol and make the solution alkaline by adding 2 N sodium hydroxide. Phthalates produce a deep blue color.

Succinic acid may be identified by reacting a small amount of the resin (or 3–4 drops of the available solution) with about 1 g hydroquinone and 2 ml concentrated sulfuric acid. Heat this over a small flame to approximately 190°C. Cool and dilute the sample with 25 ml water, and then shake it with about 50 ml benzene. The presence of succinic acid is confirmed when the solution turns red. Wash the benzene phase with water and react it with 0.1 N sodium hydroxide. A blue color results. This test may not be definite because of phthalic acid interference.

Maleic acid resins give a wine red to olive brown color in the Liebermann-Storch-Morawski reaction (see Section 6.1.1).

Polyethylene terephthalate and *polybutylene terephthalate* are soluble in nitrobenzene. For their identification, pyrolyze a small sample in a glass tube covered with filter paper. First drench the filter paper with a saturated solution of *o*-nitrobenzaldehyde in dilute sodium hydroxide. A blue-green color (indigo), which is stable against dilute hydrochloric acid, indicates terephthalic acid.

The absolute distinction between polyethylene terephthalate (PET) and polybutylene terephthalate (PBT) is difficult using simple methods. PET melts at 250–260°C, PBTP at about 220°C. However, additives may cause deviations from these melting points.

PETP and PBTP can be identified by a white sublimate when these polymers are heated in a combustion tube.

6.2.16   Cellulose Derivatives

Cellulose acetate is the most well known plastic with a cellulose base. Others are cellulose acetobutyrate and cellulose propionate. Cellulose hydrate may be used as a vulcanized fiber. Cellulose may be identified fairly simply. Dissolve or suspend a sample in acetone, react it with 2–3 drops of a 2% solution of α-naphthol in ethanol, and carefully introduce a layer of concentrated sulfuric acid under this. At the phase boundary, a red to red-brown ring forms. In the presence of cellulose nitrate, a green ring forms. Sugars and lignin produce interference. For differentiation between cellulose acetate and cellulose acetatobutyrate, it is usually sufficient to examine the vapors produced by dry heating of the sample. The acetate smells like acetic acid; the acetobutyrate smells of both acetic acid and butyric acid (like rancid butter).

For identification of cellulose acetates or propionates one can use the reaction with lanthanum nitrate. In this test one adds one or two drops of a 50% aqueous lanthanum nitrate solution and one drop of a 0.1 N iodine solution to a small amount of the polymer sample on a spot test plate. Then a drop of concentrated ammonia is added. If cellulose acetates are present one quickly observes a blue coloration; with cellulose propionate the coloration is brown.

Cellulose nitrates may be recognized by the above reactions and by the sensitive diphenylamine test. Heat a sample with 0.5 N aqueous potassium hydroxide (dissolve 1.8 g potassium hydroxide in 100 ml water) or 0.5 N sodium hydroxide for a few minutes and then acidify this with dilute sulfuric acid. Separate the supernatant liquid from the residue. Layer a solution of 10 mg diphenylamine in 10 ml concentrated sulfuric acid on top of that. A blue ring at the interface indicates cellulose nitrate. In order to identify nitrocellulose lacquers on cellophane, dissolve a few crystals of diphenylamine in 0.5 ml concentrated sulfuric acid and add a few drops of this to the sample. A blue color is a positive test.

6.2.17 Silicones

Silicones are produced in the form of resins, oils, greases, and also as rubberlike elastic products. These materials also appear as processing aids in the manufacture of plastics, as impregnation compounds, coatings, separating materials, mold releases, etc. They can be identified because they contain the element silicon. To test for silicon, mix approximately 30 mg of the sample with 100 mg sodium carbonate and 10 mg sodium peroxide. Heat this in a platinum or nickel crucible over a flame. Dissolve the melt in a few drops of water, boil it, and then add dilute nitric acid until the solution is neutral or slightly acidic. The identification of silicon then follows in the usual way with the addition of a few drops of ammonium molybdate. (See Chapter 4.)

6.2.18 Rubberlike Plastics

Although, strictly speaking, rubbers should not be classed as plastics, we would like to consider the most important types here since their areas of application overlap with those of plastics. Butyl rubber (polyisobutylene with some isoprene repeat units) can be identified with mercury(II) oxide (see 6.2.1). Polybutadiene and polyisoprene contain double bonds, which can be identified using Wijs solution. This reagent solution is obtained by dissolving 6–7 ml of pure iodine monochloride in glacial acetic acid (up to 1 liter). The solution must be kept in the dark and has only a limited lifetime. To test the polymer, dissolve it in carbon tetrachloride or molten p-dichlorobenzene (melting point 50 °C) and react it dropwise with the reagent. Double bonds discolor the solution. This method is not specific for rubber but applies in general to all unsaturated polymers.

Use the Burchfield color reaction to differentiate between different types of rubber (see Table 15). Heat 0.5 g of the sample in a test tube. Pass the pyrolysis vapors into 1.5 ml of the reagent described below. Observe the color, and then dilute the solution with 5 ml of methanol and boil it for 3 min.

Reagent. Dissolve 1 g *p*-dimethylaminobenzaldehyde and 0.01 g hydroquinone by heating them gently in 100 ml methanol. Then react solution with 5 ml concentrated hydrochloric acid and 10 ml ethylene glycol. This reagent can be kept for several months in a brown bottle.

Table 15. Burchfield Color Reaction to Distinguish between Elastomers

Elastomer	On Contact of the Pyrolysis Vapors with Reagent	After Subsequent Boiling and Addition of Methanol
None (blank test)	Yellowish	Yellowish
Natural rubber (polyisoprene)	Yellow brown	Green-violet-blue
Polybutadiene	Light green	Blue green
Butyl rubber	Yellow	Yellow brown to weakly violet blue
Styrene-butadiene copolymers	Yellow green	Green
Butadiene-acrylonitrile copolymers	Orange red	Red to red brown
Polychloroprene	Yellow green	Yellowish green
Silicone rubber	Yellow	Yellow
Polyurethane elastomers	Yellow	Yellow

7 Chemicals

The chemicals needed to carry out the tests described earlier are listed in this chapter. They are available from commercial suppliers. We recommend that the most important acids, bases, and solvents be ordered in at least 0.5–1-liter quantities. Dilute solutions can be prepared in the laboratory. As for indicator reagents, it is generally sufficient to order 1–5 g. For storing chemicals, use only unambiguously identified bottles unless the reagents are supplied in labeled plastic containers.

It must be pointed out again that many organic solvents are flammable and should therefore be stored in limited amounts. The use of concentrated acids and bases also requires special safety measures, since they can cause injuries to skin and eyes.

All solvents and chemicals named here are available in several degrees of purity, for example, technical, pure, chemically pure, for analysis, etc. As far as possible, use only analytically pure reagents. Solvents that have turned yellow or dark on storage should be distilled before use.

Acids and Bases

Table 16 provides directions for the preparation of the required dilute solutions from the commercially available concentrated solutions. If it is not otherwise indicated, the dilute solutions used in this book refer to approximately 2 normal (2 N) solutions. In diluting a concentrated acid or base, always add the acid or base to the required amount of distilled or deionized water, never the other way around, since the resulting heat can lead to spattering. *(Always wear safety glasses!)*

Table 16. Concentrations of Commercially Available Acids and Bases

Acid or Base	Content in		
	Weight %	Mol/ liter	Nor- mality
Concentrated sulfuric acid ($d = 1.84$ g/cm^3)	96		37
Dilute sulfuric acid	9	1	2
Fuming nitric acid	86		
Concentrated nitric acid ($d = 1.40$ g/cm^3)	65	10	10
Dilute nitric acid	12	2	2
Fuming hydrochloric acid ($d = 1.19$ g/cm^3)	38	12.5	12.5
Concentrated hydrochloric acid ($d = 1.16$ g/cm^3)	32	10	10
Dilute hydrochloric acid	7	2	2
Glacial acetic acid (water-free)	100		17
Dilute acetic acid	12	2	2
Dilute sodium hydroxide	7.5	2	2
Concentrated ammonia	25	13	6.5
Dilute ammonia	3.5	2	2

Dilute solutions are prepared in the laboratory according to the following directions:

Dilute sulfuric acid: 5 ml concentrated acid ($d = 1.84$ g/cm^3) in 90 ml water

Dilute nitric acid: 13 ml concentrated acid ($d = 1.40$ g/cm^3) in 80 ml water

Dilute hydrochloric acid: 19 ml concentrated acid ($d = 1.16$ g/cm^3) in 80 ml water

Dilute acetic acid: 12 ml glacial acetic acid
   in 88 ml water
Dilute ammonia: 17 ml concentrated ammonia
   ($d = 0.882$ g/cm^3) in 90 ml water
Dilute sodium hydroxide: Dissolve 8 g hydroxide
   in 100 ml water

In addition to the acids and bases mentioned in
Table 14 you will often need:
Acetic anhydride
Formic acid
3% Hydrogen peroxide

For the preparation of all aqueous solutions, always
use distilled or deionized water, never tap water. Polyethylene squeeze bottles (250 ml capacity) are usually
very practical, since they are very suitable for the storage of distilled water and methanol.

Inorganic Chemicals

Zinc chloride, anhydrous   ⎫ for density
Magnesium chloride, anhydrous ⎬ determination
Iron(II) sulfate   ⎭
Iron(III) chloride (1.5 *N* solution in water)
Sodium nitroprussate
Lead acetate as a 2 *N* solution
   (26.7 g to 100 g of water)
Silver nitrate as a 2% solution (store in the dark)
Calcium chloride
Sodium hydroxide
Ammonium molybdate
Ammonium sulfate
Sodium carbonate (anhydrous)

Sodium hydroxide
Sodium peroxide
Sodium nitrite
Sodium acetate
Sodium thiosulfate
Sodium hypochlorite or chloride of lime solution
Barium chloride
Potassium hydroxide (2.8 g to 100 g water)
Mercury(II) oxide
Nickel sulfate
Copper(II) acetate
Lanthanum nitrate
Borax
Barium hydroxide solution,
    approximately 0.2 N (1.7 g to 100 g water)
Sodium or potassium under petroleum
    or some other inert liquid
Iodine
0.1 N iodine-potassium iodide solution: dissolve 16.7 g
    potassium iodide in 200 ml water, then dissolve
    12.7 g of iodine in this solution and dilute the mix-
    ture with water to 1000 ml)
Wijs solution or iodine monochloride (see Section
6.2.18)

Organic Solvents

Not all the organic solvents listed in Table 7 are neces-
sary. The supply can be limited to the following:
Benzene
Toluene
p-Xylene
Nitrobenzene
n-Hexane or petroleum ether

Cyclohexanone
Tetrahydrofuran
Dioxane
Diethyl ether
Formamide
Dimethylformamide
Dimethylsulfoxide
Chloroform
Carbon tetrachloride
Methanol
Ethanol
Ethylene glycol
Acetone
Ethyl acetate
m-Cresol
Benzyl alcohol
Benzylamine
Pyridine

Organic Reagents

The preparation of necessary solutions is described in
the text. Many solutions can be stored for a limited
time only and therefore they should be prepared fresh
when necessary.
Benzidine
Diphenylamine
Chromotropic acid
Thymol
Morpholine
Hydroquinone
o-Nitrobenzaldehyde
p-Dimethylaminobenzaldehyde
2,6-Dibromoquinone-4-chloroimide
α-Naphthol

4-Nitrobenzodiazoniumfluoroborate
   (Nitrazol CF-extra)
Phenylhydrazine
Urease

Miscellaneous

Litmus paper (red and blue)
Congo red paper
pH paper, as a universal paper for many experiments
Lead acetate paper (keep in a closed bottle)
Cotton wool
Glass wool
Fine sand
Silver coin (for sulfur identification)
Copper wire
Active charcoal

8 Laboratory Aids and Equipment

The tests described in this book do not require any apparatus or equipment other than normal laboratory equipment. The following list contains what might have to be ordered if a laboratory is not available.

For heating, use a hot plate or a heating mantle whenever possible. Open flames, a Bunsen burner, or, if there is no gas connection, an alcohol or Sterno burner should be used only when it is necessary to heat the samples in test tubes or pyrolysis tubes. For flame tests, a candle is sufficient.

Basic Equipment

Safety glasses
Test tubes, small, approximately 7 mm in diameter
    medium, approximately 15 mm diameter
Corks or rubber stoppers to fit the test tubes
Beakers, 50, 100, 250, 1000 ml
Glass funnels,
    approximately 4 and 7 cm in diameter
Watch glasses
Combustion tubes, approximately 8×70 mm
Glass rods
Graduated cylinders, 10 ml, 100 ml, 500 ml
Pipets, 1 ml, 10 ml
Porcelain mortar with pestle,
    approximately 10 cm in diameter

Porcelain plate
Porcelain cups, approximately 5 cm in diameter
Porcelain crucible,
    approximately 3–3.5 cm in diameter
Platinum or nickel crucible,
    approximately 3 cm in diameter
Aerometer for density measurement
    in the range 0.8–2.2 g/cm^3
A small balance
    (if nothing better is available,
    a letter scale is sufficient)
Test tube rack
Test tube tongs
Crucible tongs
Tweezers
Spatula
Knife
Filter paper in sheets and round filter paper
    for the funnels
Oil bath of metal (best, a silicon oil)

Optional Equipment

Mill for grinding plastic samples
Heating mantles and a stand with clamps
Distillation flask, reflux condenser (see Fig. 9)
Soxhlet apparatus with tubes for extraction (see Fig. 2)
Hot stage (see Fig. 6) or melting point microscope.

9 Guide to Further Reading

L. S. Bark, N. S. Allen (Eds.): *Analysis of Polymer Systems.* Applied Science Publishers Ltd., London, 1982.

T. R. Crompton: *Chemical Analysis of Additives in Plastics,* 2nd Ed., Pergamon, Oxford, New York, 1977.

J. Haslam, H. A. Willis and D. C. M. Squirrel: *Identification and Analysis of Plastics,* 2nd Ed., Butterworth, London, 1972; Paperback Reprint Edition, Heyden & Son, London and Philadelphia, 1980.

D. O. Hummel, F. Scholl: *Atlas of Polymer and Plastics Analysis,* 2nd Revised Ed. (3 vols.): Vol. 1: Polymers, Structures and Spectra. Vol. 2 a: Plastics, Fibers, Rubbers, Resins, Starting and Auxiliary Materials, Degradation Products. Vol. 2 b: Spectra. Vol. 3: Additives and Processing Aids. Carl Hanser Verlag, Munich, Vienna/VCH (Verlag Chemie) Weinheim, New York, 1978, 1981, 1985, 1986.

G. Kämpf: *Characterization of Plastics by Physical Methods.* Experimental Techniques and Practical Applications. Hanser, Munich, Vienna, 1986. (Distributed by Macmillan Publishing Co. in USA and Collier-Macmillan in Canada).

G. M. Kline, (Ed.): High Polymers, Vol. XII, *Analytical Chemistry of Polymers.* (3 Parts). Interscience, New York, 1959, 1962. (John Wiley & Sons).

A. Krause, A. Lange and M. Ezrin: *Plastics Analysis Guide.* Chemical and Instrumental Methods.

Hanser, Munich, Vienna, 1983. (Distributed by Maxmillan Publishing Co. in USA and Collier-Macmillan in Canada).

J. Mitchell, Jr. (Ed.): *Applied Polymer Analysis and Characterization.* Hanser, Munich, Vienna, 1987. (Distributed by Macmillan Publishing Co. in USA and Collier-Macmillan in Canada).

E. Schröder: *Guide to Polymer Characterization.* Hanser, Munich, Vienna, (1988). (Distributed by Macmillan Publishing Co. in the USA and Collier-Macmillan in Canada).

W. C. Wake: *Analysis of Rubbers and Rubber-like Polymers.* 2nd Ed., Maclaren, London 1969.

10 Polymer Acronyms

ABR	Acrylate-butadiene rubber
ABS	Acrylonitrile-butadiene-styrene rubber
ACM	Acrylate rubber
AES	Acrylonitrile-ethylene-propylene-styrene quater-polymer
AMMA	Acrylonitrile-methyl methacrylate copolymer
ANM	Acrylonitrile-acrylate rubber
APP	Atactic polypropylene
ASA	Acrylonitrile-styrene-acrylate terpolymer
BIIR	Brominated isobutene-isoprene (butyl) rubber
BR	Cis-1,4-butadiene rubber (cis-1,4-polybutadiene)
BS	Butadiene-styrene copolymer (see also SB)
CA	Cellulose acetate
CAB	Cellulose acetate-butyrate
CAP	Cellulose acetate-propionate
CF	Cresol-formaldehyde resin
CHC	Epichlorohydrin-ethylene oxide rubber
CHR	Epichlorohydrin rubber (see also CO)
CMC	Carboxymethyl cellulose
CN	Cellulose nitrate (see also NC)
CNR	Carboxynitroso rubber; (tetrafluoroethylene-tri-fluoronitrosomethane-unsat.monomer terpolymer)
CO	Poly[(chloromethyl)oxirane]; epichlorohydrin rubber (see also CHR)
CP	Cellulose propionate
CPE	Chlorinated polyethylene
CR	Chloroprene rubber
CS	Casein
CSM	Chlorosulfonated polyethylene
CTA	Cellulose triacetate
CTFE	Poly(chlorotrifluoroethylene); (see also PCTFE)
EAA	Ethylene-acrylic acid copolymer
EAM	Ethylene-vinyl acetate copolymer

EC	Ethyl cellulose
ECB	Ethylene copolymer blends with bitumen
ECTFE	Ethylene-chlorotrifluoroethylene copolymer
EEA	Ethylene-ethyl acrylate copolymer
EMA	Ethylene-methacrylic acid copolymer
	or ethylene-maleic anhydride copolymer
EP	Epoxy resin
E/P	Ethylene-propylene copolymer (see also EPM, EPR)
EPDM	Ethylene-propylene-nonconjugated diene terpolymer (see also EPT)
EPE	Epoxy resin ester
EPM	Ethylene-propylene rubber (see also E/P, EPR)
EPR	Ethylene-propylene rubber (see also E/P, EPM)
EPS	Expanded polystyrene; polystyrene foam (see also XPS)
EPT	Ethylene-propylene-diene terpolymer (see also EPDM)
ETFE	Ethylene-tetrafluoroethylene copolymer
EVA, E/VAC	Ethylene-vinyl acetate copolymer
EVE	Ethylene-vinyl ether copolymer
FE	Fluorine-containing elastomer
FEP	Tetrafluoroethylene-hexafluoropropylene rubber; see PFEP
FF	Furan-formaldehyde resins
FPM	Vinylidene fluoride-hexafluoropropylene rubber
FSI	Fluorinated silicone rubber
GR-I	Butyl rubber (former US acronym) (see also IIR, PIBI)
GR-N	Nitrile rubber (former US acronym) (see also NBR)
GR-S	Styrene-butadiene rubber (former US acronym; see PBS, SBR)
HDPE	High density polyethylene
HEC	Hydroxyethylcellulose
HIPS	High impact polystyrene
HMWPE	High molecular weight polyethylene
IIR	Isobutene-isoprene rubber; butyl rubber (see also GR-I, PIBI)
IPN	Interpenetrating polymer network
IR	Synthetic cis-1,4-polyisoprene

LDPE	Low density polyethylene
LLDPE	Linear low density polyethylene
MABS	Methyl methacrylate-acrylonitrile-butadiene-sty-rene
MBS	Methyl methacrylate-butadiene-styrene terpolymer
MC	Methyl cellulose
MDPE	Medium density polyethylene (ca. 0.93–0.94 g/cm^3)
MF	Melamine-formaldehyde resin
MPF	Melamine-phenol-formaldehyde resin
NBR	Acrylonitrile-butadiene rubber; nitrile rubber; GR-I
NC	Nitrocellulose; cellulose nitrate (see also CN)
NCR	Acrylonitrile-chloroprene rubber
NIR	Acrylonitrile-isoprene rubber
NR	Natural rubber (cis-1,4-polyisoprene)
OER	Oil extended rubber
OPR	Propylene oxide rubber
PA	Polyamide (e.g. PA 6,6 = polyamide 6,6 = nylon 6,6 in US literature)
PAA	Poly(acrylic acid)
PAI	Polyamide-imide
PAMS	Poly(alpha-methylstyrene)
PAN	Polyacrylonitrile (fiber)
PARA	Poly(arylamide)
PB	Poly(1-butene)
PBI	Poly(benzimidazoles)
PBMA	Poly(n-butyl methacrylate)
PBR	Butadiene-vinyl pyridine copolymer
PBS	Butadiene-styrene copolymer (see also GR-S, SBR)
PBT, PBTP	Poly(butylene terephthalate)
PC, PCO	Polycarbonate
PCD	Poly(carbodiimide)
PCTFE	Poly(chlorotrifluoroethylene)
PDAP	Poly(diallyl phthalate)
PDMS	Poly(dimethylsiloxane)
PE	Polyethylene
PEA	Poly(ethyl acrylate)

PEC	Chlorinated polyethylene (see also CPE)
PEEK	Poly(arylether ketone)
PEI	Poly(ether imide)
PEO, PEOX	Poly(ethylene oxide)
PEP	Ethylene-propylene polymer (see also E/P, EPR)
PEPA	Polyether-polyamide block copolymer
PES	Polyethersulfone
PET, PETP	Poly(ethylene terephthalate)
PF	Phenol-formaldehyde resin
PFA	Perfluoroalkoxy resins
PFEP	Tetrafluoroethylene-hexafluoropropylene copolymer; FEP
PI	Polyimide
PIB	Polyisobutylene
PIBI	Isobutene-isoprene copolymer; butyl rubber; GR-I, IIR
PIBO	Poly(isobutylene oxide)
PIP	Synthetic poly-cis-1,4-polyisoprene; (also CPI, IR)
PIR	Polyisocyanurate
PMA	Poly(methyl acrylate)
PMI	Polymethacrylimide
PMMA	Poly(methyl methacrylate)
PMMI	Polypyromellitimide
PMP	Poly(4-methyl-1-pentene)
PO	Poly(propylene oxide); or polyolefins; or phenoxy resins
POM	Polyoxymethylene, polyformaldehyde
POP	Poly(phenylene oxide) (also PPO/PPE)
PP	Polypropylene
PPC	Chlorinated polypropylene
PPE	Poly(phenylene ether)
PPMS	Poly(para-methylstyrene)
PPO	Poly(phenylene oxide) (also PPO/PPE)
PPOX	Poly(propylene oxide)
PPS	Poly(phenylene sulfide)
PPSU	Poly(phenylene sulfone)
PPT	Poly(propylene terephthalate)
PS	Polystyrene
PSB	Styrene-butadiene rubber (see GR-S, SBR)
PSF, PSO	Polysulfone
PSU	Poly(phenylene sulfone)
PTFE	Poly(tetrafluoroethylene)
P3FE	Poly(trifluoroethylene)

PTMT	Poly(tetramethylene terephthalate)
	= poly(butylene terephthalate) (see also PBTP)
PUR	Polyurethane
PVA, PVAC	Poly(vinyl acetate)
PVAL	Poly(vinyl alcohol) (also PVOH)
PVB	Poly(vinyl butyral)
PVC	Poly(vinyl chloride)
PVCA	Vinyl chloride-vinyl acetate copolymer
	(also PVCAC)
PVCC	Chlorinated poly(vinyl chloride)
PVDC	Poly(vinylidene chloride)
PVDF	Poly(vinylidene fluoride)
PVF	Poly(vinyl fluoride)
PVFM	Poly(vinyl formal) (also PVFO)
PVI	Poly(vinyl isobutyl ether)
PVK	Poly(N-vinylcarbazole)
PVP	Poly(N-vinylpyrrolidone)
RF	Resorcinol-formaldehyde resin
SAN	Styrene-acrylonitrile copolymer
SB	Styrene-butadiene copolymer
SBR	Styrene-butadiene rubber (see also GR-S)
SCR	Styrene-chloroprene rubber
S-EPDM	Sulfonated ethylene-propylene-diene terpolymers
SHIPS	Super-high impact polystyrene
SI	Silicone resins; poly(dimethylsiloxane)
SIR	Styrene-isoprene rubber
SMA	Styrene-maleic anhydride copolymer
SMS	Styrene-alpha-methylstyrene copolymer
TPE	Thermoplastic elastomer
TPR	1,5-trans-Poly(pentenamer)
TPU	Thermoplastic polyurethane
TPX	Poly(methyl pentene)
UF	Urea-formaldehyde resins
UHMW-PE	Ultrahigh molecular weight poly(ethylene)
	(also UHMPE)
	(molecular mass over 3.1×10^{6} g/mol)
UP	Unsaturated polyester
VC/E	Vinyl chloride-ethylene copolymer

VC/E/VA	Vinyl chloride-ethylene-vinyl acetate copolymer
VC/MA	Vinyl chloride-methyl acrylate copolymer
VC/MMA	Vinyl chloride-methyl methacrylate copolymer
VC/OA	Vinyl chloride-octyl acrylate
VC/VAC	Vinyl chloride-vinyl acetate copolymer
VC/VDC	Vinyl chloride-vinylidene chloride
VF	Vulcan fiber
XLPE	Crosslinked polyethylene
XPS	Expandable or expanded polystyrene; (see also EPS)

Index

PIT is the abbreviation for the Plastics Identification Table which is in the pocket of the inner back cover. The numbers in brackets refer to the first column.

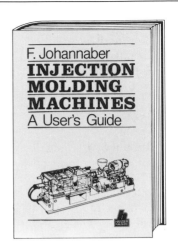

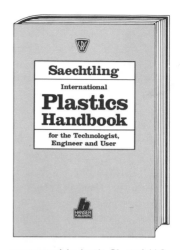